Slimming World
extra easy
entertaining

because you're amazing

fantastic food
to enjoy with
family and friends

a warm Slimming World *welcome…*

…to **Extra Easy Entertaining**. Packed with fabulous, filling recipes, this book is perfect for anyone who wants to enjoy good food and fun with family and friends – and stay smiling at the scales!

Making life easier for slimmers has been my joy and passion ever since I founded Slimming World 44 years ago. People with weight problems, as I know from my own personal struggle, have so many burdens to carry. I don't just mean the risks to physical health – which can be devastating – but also the negative effects that being overweight can have on everything we do, from struggling to find clothes that fit to missing out on fulfilling relationships, work and social life.

Having tried many diets myself, without any lasting success, I concluded long ago that the hunger, deprivation and guilt they induced were not the answer. No diet that made me miss my favourite meals, give up my favourite foods, eat separately from my family or have no social life was going to work for me!

I wanted an easy, flexible way of eating. I wanted freedom from the fear of hunger and freedom from the stress of obsessively counting calories. And I wanted support from people who truly understood how it feels to be overweight and wanted to change my life. That was my vision for slimmers when Slimming World welcomed its first members, and it is still at the heart of everything we do today.

It seems too good to be true, that you can eat as much as you like of foods you love, and lose weight – but Food Optimising isn't magic; it's based on sound scientific research into how our appetite works and how we can satisfy it without gaining weight. At Slimming World we also have a deep psychological understanding of how it feels to have a weight loss problem. And – vitally and uniquely – how to support and motivate you every step of the way.

We now have almost 10,000 groups in the UK and Ireland, all run by highly trained Consultants who have been members themselves and who know exactly how it feels to take that first step. I couldn't be more proud of them and know that they feel so privileged, as I do, to be able to support the hundreds of thousands of slimmers who trust us with their hopes and dreams each week.

When we talk about support at Slimming World, we don't mean tea and sympathy! We have a uniquely powerful way of helping members to make smarter choices for themselves, changing their relationship with food and how they see themselves. We call it IMAGE Therapy (it stands for Individual Motivation And Group Experience), and it's effective, fast and fun!

Each week our members are encouraged to set targets for the week ahead, to think through what might get in their way and plan ways to overcome these obstacles. The whole group plays a part in celebrating successes, suggesting ideas and supporting anyone who's struggling. No-one's weight is ever revealed (unless they specifically ask us to) because confidentiality is one of the keys to feeling safe. Judging people, or putting them down in any way, is completely out too, and one of our most important rules for our groups at Slimming World. Compassion, understanding, sensitivity and deeply effective motivation are what make us simply the best.

It's so inspiring to see how members thrive in this warm and nurturing atmosphere, as they discover in themselves the power to change the habits of a lifetime, and achieve goals they could never have imagined before.

With Food Optimising and IMAGE Therapy, members find they have the tools they need to maximise their choice power, and are delighted to find that losing weight becomes not only so much easier, but so much more enjoyable than they ever thought possible. As an extra motivator, members are also encouraged to put some Body Magic into their lives once they are away from the group. Body Magic is how we describe the fantastic boost to physical and mental wellbeing that extra activity can add to the Slimming World experience. Just as Food Optimising is all about choice, Body Magic is about finding ways to get moving, from formal exercise like gym classes to everyday activities like housework or dog-walking – any activity that you find enjoyable and easy to stick to, the key factor in making regular activity a lifelong habit.

At Slimming World, we never take success for granted and we're always looking for ways to improve our service, to inspire members even further and make their weight loss journey even more exciting, rewarding and successful. Your life and your success is the focus of our lives.

I'm so thrilled to present *Extra Easy Entertaining*, the latest addition to our famous library of great eating experiences. It's full of delicious inspiration – recipes that really do work and that you'll love to cook, eat and share with the people you care about. If you're already a member of our Slimming World family, I hope it gives you even more exciting Food Optimising ideas. And if you haven't yet joined us at Slimming World, we look forward to welcoming you very soon! You're just one step away from finding the weight loss plan that will change your life.

With warmest wishes from the club with the big heart and from me,

Margaret Miles-Bramwell OBE HonMUniv FRSA
Founder and Chairman

introducing
extra easy
entertaining

They say that sharing a meal and a laugh with the people you love is one of life's greatest pleasures and, at Slimming World, we couldn't agree more!

We enjoy socialising every bit as much as you do and we believe that whether you're wining and dining your partner, preparing an impromptu family dinner or hosting the party of the century, good food should never be off the menu! We also believe that you shouldn't have to miss out because you're watching your weight. And that's why we've created *Extra Easy Entertaining*.

Extra Easy Entertaining is a stunning collection of more than 100 recipes that will kick your hospitality – and your slimming campaign – into high-gear! From light lunches and lazy brunches to quick, casual suppers, party buffets (all you can eat-style!) and formal occasions when you want to cook to impress, this book has every social situation covered! And because all our recipes are deliciously easy to prepare you'll spend less time in the kitchen and more time being the host(ess) with the most(est)!

Make your dream 'do' a reality with:

● Classy canapés and cocktails

● Bite-sized nibbles and finger food plus gourmet salads, meats and treats to upscale buffets, barbecues and picnics

● Easy appetisers, mighty main courses, sumptuous sides and dazzling desserts – mix and match them and keep your menus fresh and varied forever more!

Your guests will never believe that you can enjoy all these delicious dishes on a regular basis and lose weight – yet it's true! You can cook the meals in *Extra Easy Entertaining* every day, safe in the knowledge that you will be following a healthy, nutritious, effective weight loss plan.

Welcome to *Extra Easy Entertaining*; we're sure you'll love it as an excellent source of inspiration and ideas! Enjoy the cooking and the compliments as you serve these dishes at your gatherings all year round!

Read on to find out more about Food Optimising and everything that Slimming World has to offer!

For details of a warm and friendly group near you, call 0844 897 8000 or visit www.slimmingworld.com

discover
Food Optimising

At Slimming World we love celebrations – in fact we're famous for them! And our revolutionary weight loss plan, Food Optimising, gives us plenty of reasons to celebrate every single day…

As you'll see as you browse through the recipes in this gorgeous book, with Food Optimising you really can enjoy fabulous filling food, treat yourself every day and still lose weight steadily until you reach your dream weight – and stay slim and healthy for life.

That's because, unlike typical diets, Food Optimising works in harmony with your natural appetite and love of food. At Slimming World we encourage members to enjoy eating without feeling guilty, which is so often the damaging result of following faddy diets that are awkward to follow and hard to stick to.

Food Optimising is based on the sound scientific principle that to lose weight you have to eat less energy (in the form of calories) than you use. Typical diets go about restricting your energy intake in various ways, for instance by making you count every calorie you eat, by banning high calorie foods, or imposing restrictions such as not eating different types of food together.

Slimming World couldn't be more different – it's light years ahead, and we're with you all the way, no matter how much weight you have to lose.

No weighing, no measuring, no counting… no kidding!

Food Optimising is based on the principles of energy density – which means choosing foods that are naturally low in calories and also really filling. We call these Free Foods and they are the master-stroke of genius that makes Food Optimising so fast, effective and easy. Free Foods sweep away all the fear of hunger, worry about over-eating and the stress of counting calories that are the downfall of so many unsuccessful slimmers. Eat as much Free Food as you like and as often as you like without ever having to worry about weighing or measuring. Fill up on Free Foods – make meals from them, rely on them and enjoy them day and night to satisfy your hunger! You get the picture that we're really passionate about Free Food?

So what are these magical Free Foods? Amazingly, they're ordinary everyday foods, like lean meat and fish, fruit and vegetables, pasta and potatoes – nothing faddy or difficult to find in the shops, and not expensive ready-made meals.

Research into the science of appetite, some of which Slimming World has sponsored, shows that protein-rich and carbohydrate-rich foods like lean meat, beans, eggs, fat free dairy products, potatoes, rice and noodles are more satisfying and filling than foods that are high in fat and sugar. Nearly all fruit and vegetables are Free Foods too – they tend to be relatively low in calories for their weight so they're full of filling power as well as valuable vitamins, minerals and fibre. By basing meals on the huge range of Free Foods, Food Optimisers naturally reduce their energy intake without feeling hungry or counting a single calorie – resulting in week after week of delicious meals and steady weight loss that feels almost effortless.

The key to successful Food Optimising is to make Free Foods work for you. Eat these in unlimited amounts and they'll keep you satisfied, even on your hungriest days. They are the secret of long-term success.

Everyday extras

As well as Free Foods, Food Optimising has two other vital elements: Healthy Extras and Syns.

Healthy Extras are foods rich in nutrients that are essential to good health, such as calcium or dietary fibre, which is important for weight loss and your health. They are the next step to success! Each day, Food Optimisers choose measured servings of Healthy Extra foods, for example, wholemeal bread, cereal, cheese or milk – perfect for a balanced diet and enjoying simple everyday pleasures such as a lunchtime sandwich or cereal for breakfast.

And what about Syns? Syns are the food choices (yes, even more food!) that help to make Food Optimising uniquely enjoyable and easy to stick to. Each day, Slimming World members can decide how to use their daily allocation of Syns – maybe a chocolate bar or a slice of cake, a creamy sauce with dinner, mayonnaise on a sandwich or a glass of wine – and enjoy them without ever feeling guilty or deprived.

Limiting high-risk foods with a Syn value like these – which tend to be 'energy-dense', meaning they are high in calories for their weight and are easy to overeat – means members can balance their diet for optimum weight loss and maximum enjoyment!

Together, Free Foods, Healthy Extras and Syns are an unbeatable combination that makes Food Optimising the most flexible, generous and enjoyable weight loss plan you'll find – and it's so healthy and easy to follow that once they reach target, Slimming World members happily become Food Optimisers for life!

A perfect way of eating for every preference

One aspect of Slimming World that can often surprise new members is that there are no set menus to 'stick to'. This is one reason why Food Optimising is suitable for absolutely everyone; whether you're following a special diet for health or religious reasons, are vegan or vegetarian, or have strong food likes and dislikes (and who doesn't?), there are still so many options for making tasty, filling meals.

Food Optimising offers a number of choices to help members find the style of eating that works with their lifestyle – and the easiest of all is, unbelievably, Extra Easy!

With Extra Easy, losing weight really is easier than it's ever been before. At each meal you fill at least a third of your plate with fruit or veg and then enjoy a wide range of Free Foods – such as lean meat, poultry and fish, pasta and potatoes and beans and pulses. Add measured Healthy Extra choices and your Syns for the day and you're up and running the Extra Easy way to a great weight loss.

And you might have heard of Food Optimising's Green and Original (or Red) plans too. If you love a juicy burger, a roast dinner or a mixed grill, you'll love the Original choice. If you're a comfort-food fan, a vegetarian or vegan, and jacket potatoes, pasta dishes and rice are among your favourites, then the Green choice is designed with you in mind. You can switch between Green and Original during the week for maximum variety, or stick to Extra Easy and enjoy the best of both worlds!

Whatever you decide to do, it's true that if you Food Optimise 100% you will lose weight. And with so much choice and variety, you'll never be bored! When you join a Slimming World group, you'll find that your Consultant and fellow members will be full of foodie ideas and inspiration, and there are literally thousands of delicious Food Optimising recipes you can try in our books, magazines and online.

The club with the big heart

While this delicious collection of recipes gives you a taste of Food Optimising, the complete Slimming World experience offers so much more during your slimming journey. Our warm, practical group support and individual help for members set Slimming World apart as the organisation that really understands and, more importantly, deeply cares about your success.

IMAGE Therapy, which stands for Individual Motivation and Group Experience, is a unique support system, shared by the group yet tailored to meet each individual member's needs. Each week, every member has the opportunity to celebrate achievements, discuss challenges and share insights and milestones with their Consultant and fellow slimmers in an atmosphere that is completely safe and supportive. Many members say that IMAGE Therapy is not just their favourite part of the Slimming World meeting but the highlight of their week. IMAGE Therapy is based on a deep understanding of the psychology of slimming but it never feels like hard work; it's fun, informative, inspiring and most of all, effective at helping members see their way over obstacles and plot their path to success.

Along with Food Optimising and IMAGE Therapy, the third key element of the Slimming World experience is Body Magic – an amazing lifestyle activity programme that helps members boost their weight loss, get fit and stay slim and active for life.

As you would expect at Slimming World, Body Magic is all about choices and building active habits at your own pace – NOT about going to the gym or pushing yourself to extremes. Whether you've never exercised before or you're an avid exerciser, Body Magic starts where you are and encourages you to be a bit more active, more often.

Each week, members set their own activity goals and are supported and rewarded at every stage with awards: Bronze, Silver, Gold and Platinum. Any form of activity counts, from brisk walking, running and swimming and formal sports to vigorous household chores or dancing in front of the TV, and the more active you get, the more Body Magic awards you can pick up along the way! Ultimately, the aim is to find activities that you enjoy and can stick to, which is key to making healthy changes that will last a lifetime.

Together, this magic mix of Food Optimising (for people who love to eat!), uplifting and supportive IMAGE Therapy (which sets members up for a fabulous week – every week), and Body Magic (which empowers members to take small steps towards a more active lifestyle) is what makes Slimming World different to anything else out there! It has already helped millions of men and women lose weight and live happily (and healthily) ever after!

We hope you'll love creating the dishes in Extra Easy Entertaining as much as we did, and that they whet your appetite for the whole Slimming World experience. Your journey, your slim new life, really does start here, so come along and join in the fun – we guarantee you'll soon have plenty of your own reasons to celebrate too!

lazy brunch

Treat yourself to a relaxing morning with family or friends with these fabulously filling ideas for feel-good food. Here's the best of the brunch…

bircher
muesli

serves 4

each serving is:

3½ **Syns** on Extra Easy

3½ **Syns** on Green

3½ **Syns** on Original

preparation time: 15 minutes
plus chilling

cooking time: none

50g porridge oats

juice of 1 orange

1 tbsp sweetener,
plus extra to taste

3 apples

400g fat free natural yogurt

a few drops of vanilla essence

200g drained, canned apricots
in natural juice, thinly sliced

200g blackberries

For a deliciously healthy start to the day, try some real 'oat' cuisine! This classic Swiss-inspired recipe combines orange-soaked oats with fresh fruits to create a unique breakfast that's naturally light and sweet.

Place the oats in a large bowl, pour over 200ml of cold water and stir in the orange juice and sweetener. Cover and leave in the fridge for 2 hours or overnight if time permits.

When ready to eat, peel, core and grate one of the apples and slice the remaining two.

Mix the yogurt with the vanilla essence and sweetener to taste. Stir the grated apple into the oat mixture with half of the yogurt.

Transfer the muesli into individual bowls and top with the sliced apples and apricots and the blackberries. Divide the remaining yogurt between the bowls and serve.

The muesli can be kept in the fridge for a few days – stir in the apple just before you eat it.

tropical fruit pots

serves 4

each serving is:

1½ Syns on Extra Easy

1½ Syns on Green

1½ Syns on Original

preparation time: 15 minutes plus optional chilling

cooking time: none

---

2 passion fruit

400g mango flesh, cut into 1.5cm dice

200g pineapple flesh, cut into 1.5cm dice

2 kiwi fruit, peeled and cut into 1.5cm dice

400g fat free natural yogurt

1 tsp sweetener

a few drops of vanilla essence

25g granola

Guaranteed to add a little sunshine to your morning, these little pots of love are packed with colourful fruits and topped with creamy yogurt and crunchy cereal. This is a delicious, nutritious breakfast that the whole family will enjoy!

Halve the passion fruit and scoop out the pulp and seeds into a large bowl.

Add the mango, pineapple and kiwi fruit to the bowl and toss to mix well.

Mix the yogurt with the sweetener and vanilla essence until smooth.

Divide the fruit mixture between four dessert glasses or small bowls and top with the yogurt (you can chill the mixture in the fridge for 2-3 hours at this point, if you like).

Sprinkle over the granola just before serving.

No need to stick to the fruits listed in the recipe – mix it up and use whatever you have in your fruit bowl.

fancy
french toast

serves 4

each serving is:

4 Syns on Extra Easy

4 Syns on Green

4 Syns on Original

preparation time: 10 minutes

cooking time: under 10 minutes

100ml skimmed milk

3 large eggs, beaten

finely grated zest of 2 clementines

2 tbsp clementine juice

3 tsp sweetener

1 tsp cinnamon

low calorie cooking spray

4 slices wholemeal bread
(from a small 400g loaf)

4 clementines, peeled
and sliced horizontally

1 level tsp icing sugar, to dust

fat free natural fromage frais,
to serve

Put a zesty twist on custardy eggy bread with this indulgent brunch-time recipe bursting with fresh clementine flavour. Speedy to make and super-satisfying, this luxurious toast promises to please the crowd.

Make the French toast by placing the milk, eggs, most of the clementine zest, the clementine juice, sweetener and cinnamon in a wide shallow bowl and whisk well.

Spray a large frying pan with low calorie cooking spray and place over a medium heat.

Dip the bread slices into the egg mixture, coating both sides, and place in the pan. Fry for 2 minutes on each side until lightly golden.

Remove the bread from the pan and slice in half diagonally. Place on serving plates, top with the sliced clementines and dust with icing sugar before serving with fromage frais and the remaining clementine zest.

mixed berry pancakes

Rise and shine the American way with these awesome fluffy and fruity pancakes. Served with summer berries and creamy fromage frais, they make a tasty alternative start to the day.

Place the berries in a bowl with the sweetener and toss to mix well. Leave to stand at room temperature for 20-30 minutes.

To make the pancakes, sift the flour into a bowl with the sweetener and a pinch of salt. Mix in the eggs, milk, orange zest and vanilla essence and whisk until smooth.

Spray a small frying pan with low calorie cooking spray and place over a high heat. Pour one-eighth of the batter into the pan to coat the bottom, tilting and swirling the pan to spread the batter.

Cook for 1-2 minutes or until lightly browned at the base then carefully flip over and cook the other side for 1-2 minutes. Remove from the pan, fold into quarters and keep warm while you make the remaining pancakes.

Serve the pancakes with the berries. They're delicious lightly dusted with icing sugar (1 Syn per level teaspoon) and served with a spoonful of fromage frais and a sprig of mint.

Top with a dollop of ice cream for a dazzling dessert.

makes 8 pancakes

each pancake is:

3½ **Syns** on Extra Easy

3½ **Syns** on Green

3½ **Syns** on Original

preparation time: 20 minutes plus standing

cooking time: about 30 minutes

400g fresh mixed berries (blackberries, blueberries, raspberries and strawberries)

1 tbsp sweetener

icing sugar, to dust (optional)

fat free natural fromage frais, to serve

fresh mint leaves, to decorate

for the pancakes

150g plain flour

1 tbsp sweetener

salt

4 large eggs, beaten

100ml skimmed milk

1 tbsp finely grated orange zest

1 tsp vanilla essence

low calorie cooking spray

luxury
eggs florentine

serves 4

each serving is:

1½ Syns on Extra Easy

1½ Syns on Original

3 Syns on Green

preparation time: 25 minutes

cooking time: 25 minutes

4 large flat or Portobello mushrooms

salt and freshly ground black pepper

low calorie cooking spray

250g baby spinach leaves

juice of ½ lemon

4 large eggs

1-2 tsp white wine vinegar

a pinch of grated nutmeg

4 slices of lean ham, all visible fat removed

8 thin slices of tomato

1 tbsp crushed pink peppercorns

for the sauce

8 tbsp fat free natural fromage frais

25g Cheddar cheese, finely grated

a pinch of mustard powder

2 tbsp freshly chopped tarragon

200ml boiling hot vegetable stock

The ultimate in comfort food, this elegant classic often features on gastropub menus – for good reason! This low-Syn version is just as tasty and perfect for an indulgent weekend brunch with family and friends. Get stuck in!

Remove the stalks from the mushrooms and place gill side up on a grill rack. Season well, lightly spray with low calorie cooking spray and cook under a preheated medium-hot grill for 3-4 minutes on each side or until just cooked through.

Meanwhile place the spinach in a large pan with the lemon juice and cook for 2 minutes until wilted. Drain off any juice, season with the nutmeg and a little salt and pepper and keep warm.

Bring a large pan of lightly salted water to the boil. Stir in the vinegar, reduce the heat to a very gentle simmer and carefully break the eggs into the water. Cover the pan and let the eggs poach on a very low heat for about 4 minutes. Remove from the heat and carefully transfer the eggs to a large bowl of cold water.

Make the sauce by placing the fromage frais in a bowl with the cheese, mustard powder and tarragon. Season to taste, add the stock and, using an electric hand whisk, blend well.

Transfer to a small saucepan and heat gently for 1-2 minutes until warm (don't let it boil or the fromage frais will curdle).

Place a mushroom on each plate and cover with a slice of ham, two slices of tomato, some spinach and finally top with a poached egg. Spoon over the tarragon sauce and serve sprinkled with the pink peppercorns.

For the best poached eggs, always use really fresh eggs.

ham and
egg cups

Make everyone happy with this easy peasy flavour-packed egg recipe. Easy enough for every day and elegant enough for entertaining, these cute little cups will get your morning off to a cracking start.

Preheat the oven to 180°C/Fan 160°C/Gas 4.

Lightly spray four holes of a deep muffin tin with low calorie cooking spray.

Spray a frying pan with low calorie cooking spray and place over a high heat. Add the spring onions and mushrooms and stir-fry for 4-5 minutes. Add the tomatoes and stir-fry for 2-3 minutes. Season to taste and remove from the heat.

Line each hole in the muffin tin with two slices of the ham, gently pressing down to create a cup, and divide the spring onion mixture between them.

Crack an egg over the top of each one, season and cook in the oven for 15-20 minutes until the eggs are cooked to your liking and serve.

serves 4

each serving is:

Free on Extra Easy

Free on Original

3 Syns on Green

preparation time: 10 minutes

cooking time: 25-30 minutes

low calorie cooking spray

4 spring onions, sliced

8 button mushrooms, roughly chopped

2 tomatoes, roughly chopped

salt and freshly ground black pepper

8 thick slices of lean ham, all visible fat removed

4 large eggs

one-pan full english brunch bake

serves 4

each serving is:

1½ Syns on Extra Easy

4½ Syns on Original

7 Syns on Green

preparation time: 20 minutes

cooking time: under 30 minutes

300g Desirée potatoes,
peeled and cut into 1.5cm cubes

low calorie cooking spray

100g lean bacon rashers, all visible
fat removed, cut into 2cm pieces

4 Sainsbury's Be Good to Yourself
Extra Lean Cumberland Sausages,
each chopped into 3 pieces

1 onion, peeled and
sliced into thick rings

200g button mushrooms, halved

8 large eggs, lightly beaten

6 tbsp very finely
chopped fresh parsley

salt and freshly ground
black pepper

200g midi plum tomatoes,
halved or quartered

25g reduced fat
Cheddar cheese, grated

Combining all the best ingredients of a traditional English breakfast in one pan, this wholesome, hearty, rustic dish is great for entertaining and it will save on time as well as washing-up!

Place the potatoes in a large saucepan of lightly salted boiling water and cook for 10-12 minutes or until just tender. Drain well and set aside.

Meanwhile spray a large frying pan with low calorie cooking spray and place over a high heat. Add the bacon, sausages, onion rings and mushrooms and stir-fry for 6-8 minutes or until lightly browned.

Add the potatoes to the mixture and stir to mix well.

Whisk the eggs with the chopped parsley and season well. Pour this over the potato mixture, scatter over the tomatoes and cook over a gentle heat for 8-10 minutes or until the base is set.

Sprinkle over the cheese and place under a preheated hot grill for 4-5 minutes or until lightly golden and set. Cut into thick wedges and serve.

For a Green day recipe, leave out the bacon and replace the sausages with four Cauldron Vegetarian Cumberland sausages – the Syn values per serving would be: 2 Syns on Extra Easy and Green, and 5 Syns on Original.

mixed
seafood kedgeree

serves 4

each serving is:

Free on Extra Easy

8½ **Syns** on Green

13 **Syns** on Original

❄ (if fish and seafood
not previously frozen)

preparation time: 30 minutes
plus standing

cooking time: under 30 minutes

200g smoked haddock fillet

200g salmon fillet

300ml fish stock

low calorie cooking spray

1 onion, peeled and finely chopped

2 tsp cumin seeds

6 green cardamom pods,
lightly crushed

1 cinnamon stick

3 cloves

1 tbsp mild curry powder

300g basmati rice

12 large raw prawns, peeled
(tails can be left on if preferred)

8 scallops, cleaned

200g green beans, trimmed
and cut into 1.5cm pieces

½ tsp ground turmeric

a small handful of freshly
chopped coriander

salt and freshly ground
black pepper

4 eggs, boiled to your liking,
peeled and halved

lemon wedges, to serve

This noble dish originates from colonial India
and combines fresh, succulent seafood with
spicy rice and veg in a flavour-packed feast fit
for a king!

Place the haddock and salmon in a large saucepan. Pour over the
stock, cover and simmer over a low heat for 5 minutes. Remove from
the heat and leave to stand, covered, for 10 minutes.

Meanwhile spray a large frying pan with low calorie cooking spray
and place over a medium heat. Add the onion, cumin seeds,
cardamom pods, cinnamon stick, cloves and curry powder and
stir-fry for 6-8 minutes or until the onion is soft.

Remove the fish from the pan with a slotted spoon, reserving the
stock and discarding any skin and bones. Transfer the fish to a
warmed plate, cover and set aside. Place the reserved stock in a jug
and make up to 650ml with water.

Rinse the rice in cold water, drain well then stir it into the onion mixture.

Pour the reserved stock into the pan, add the prawns, scallops and
green beans and stir in the turmeric.

Bring to the boil, cover tightly with a lid, reduce the heat to low and
cook gently for 10-12 minutes. Remove from the heat and allow to
stand, covered and undisturbed, for 12-15 minutes.

Fluff up the grains of rice with a fork and spoon onto a serving plate.

Break the poached haddock and salmon fillets into big pieces and stir
into the rice, scatter over the coriander and stir gently to mix without
breaking up the fish.

Check the seasoning, top with the eggs and serve with lemon wedges
to squeeze over.

smoked salmon and herb souffléd omelette

Once you've had a souffléd omelette there's no going back! Light, airy and moist, it's an impressive change to a traditional omelette and smoked salmon, dill and chives turn it into a truly luxurious treat.

Place the egg yolks in a large bowl with the soft cheese, spring onions and herbs. Season to taste and whisk until well combined, then stir in the smoked salmon.

In a separate bowl, whisk the egg whites to soft peaks then gently fold them into the egg yolk mixture.

Spray a large ovenproof frying pan with low calorie cooking spray and place over a medium heat. Pour in the egg mixture, reduce the heat to low and cook for 4-5 minutes until just set on the bottom. Do not stir.

Place the frying pan under a preheated medium-hot grill and grill for 4-5 minutes or until the top is lightly browned and just set.

Cut into slices, serve with the lemon wedges and garnish with sprigs of dill.

*For **best results** use a **good non-stick** frying pan.*

serves 4

each serving is:

1½ **Syns** on Extra Easy

1½ **Syns** on Original

8½ **Syns** on Green

preparation time: 20 minutes

cooking time: under 10 minutes

8 large eggs, separated

100g low fat soft cheese

4 spring onions, finely sliced

3 tbsp each of finely snipped chives and dill

salt and freshly ground black pepper

400g smoked salmon trimmings

low calorie cooking spray

lemon wedges, to serve

dill sprigs, to garnish

spicy baked
brunch beans

Start your day the right way with this perfect one-pan wonder. Packed with flavour, this quick and easy brunch recipe is guaranteed to leave everyone full of beans!

Spray a large frying pan with low calorie cooking spray and place over a medium heat.

Fry the onion, red chilli, peppers, garlic and ginger for 6-8 minutes or until softened.

Add the baked beans and ground cumin and heat through. Season to taste.

Remove from the heat and scatter the chopped coriander to serve.

You could top these tasty beans with eggs, either poached or fried using low calorie cooking spray.

serves 4

each serving is:

Free on Extra Easy

Free on Green

12½ Syns on Original

preparation time: 15 minutes

cooking time: under 10 minutes

low calorie cooking spray

1 onion, peeled and finely chopped

1 red chilli, deseeded and finely chopped

1 red pepper and 1 yellow pepper, deseeded and finely diced

1 garlic clove, peeled and crushed

1.5cm piece root ginger, peeled and grated

3 x 415g cans baked beans in tomato sauce

1 tsp ground cumin

salt and freshly ground black pepper

a large handful of roughly chopped fresh coriander

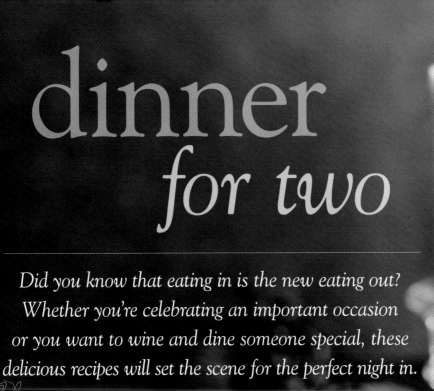

dinner
for two

*Did you know that eating in is the new eating out?
Whether you're celebrating an important occasion
or you want to wine and dine someone special, these
delicious recipes will set the scene for the perfect night in.*

warm beef and ribbon vegetable salad

serves 2

each serving is:

½ **Syn** on Extra Easy

½ **Syn** on Original

13½ **Syns** on Green

preparation time: 20 minutes

cooking time: under 10 minutes

---

for the dressing

6 tbsp light soy sauce

2 tbsp fat free French dressing

1 level tsp sweet chilli sauce

juice of 1 lime

1 tsp nam pla (Thai fish sauce)

¼ tsp sweetener

for the salad

½ red pepper, deseeded and cut into very thin strips

½ cucumber, peeled into thin ribbons (or cut into thin matchsticks)

½ carrot, peeled into thin ribbons (or cut into thin matchsticks)

4 spring onions, finely shredded

6 red radishes, very thinly sliced

400g lean sirloin or fillet steak, all visible fat removed

low calorie cooking spray

salt and freshly ground black pepper

This vibrant appetiser sets the scene for a dinner packed with colourful conversation, a touch of tenderness and even a cheeky hint of spice! Ready in under 10 minutes and served warm, it really does make the perfect starter – quick, easy and totally delicious!

First make the dressing by mixing the soy sauce, fat free dressing, sweet chilli sauce, lime juice, nam pla and sweetener together in a bowl. Set aside.

Place the red pepper, cucumber, carrot, spring onions and radishes in a wide bowl, pour over the dressing and toss to mix well.

Place the steak between two sheets of cling film and lightly beat with a rolling pin to flatten until about 1.5cm thick. Lightly spray with low calorie cooking spray and season well.

Preheat a ridged griddle until hot, add the steak and cook for 2-3 minutes on each side or until cooked to your liking. Remove from the heat, cover and leave to stand for 6-8 minutes.

Slice the steak into thin strips and place in the bowl with the vegetables, toss to mix well and serve immediately.

zesty scallop and prosciutto skewers

serves 2

each serving is:

1 Syn on Extra Easy

1 Syn on Original

8 Syns on Green

preparation time: 15 minutes

cooking time: under 10 minutes

---

for the dressing

1 garlic clove, peeled and crushed

100ml fat free French dressing

finely grated zest and juice of 1 small lemon

1 tsp finely chopped fresh rosemary

½ red chilli, deseeded and finely chopped

a small handful of finely chopped fresh basil

for the scallops

4 large slices of prosciutto or Parma ham

12 fresh scallops, cleaned

salad, to serve

Impress your 'plus one' with plump, delicate scallops wrapped in salty ham – the starter of kings! These posh skewers are cooked in minutes, leaving you with more time to enjoy the occasion.

Soak four wooden skewers in cold water for at least 30 minutes (this prevents them burning).

To make the dressing, place the garlic, fat free dressing, the lemon zest and juice, chopped rosemary, red chilli and chopped basil in a blender or food processor and pulse until just smooth. Transfer to a small bowl and set aside.

Preheat a ridged griddle to high.

Cut each slice of ham lengthways into three pieces and wrap each piece around a scallop. Thread each skewer with three of the wrapped scallops.

Place the skewers on the griddle (or under a medium-hot grill) and cook for 2-3 minutes on each side until lightly charred and cooked through.

Transfer to individual serving plates, drizzle the dressing over and serve with a side salad of your choice.

sweet potato cakes
with sweet chilli mayo

serves 2

each serving is:

2½ Syns on Extra Easy

2½ Syns on Green

8 Syns on Original

 V

preparation time: 20 minutes

cooking time: under 30 minutes

Forget the forks and create these deliciously dunkable sweet potato cakes. Finger food – especially with this mouth-wateringly delicious low-Syn mayo – has never looked or tasted so good!

for the cakes

1 sweet potato, peeled and cut into 2.5cm cubes

1 red chilli, deseeded and finely chopped

2 spring onions, very thinly sliced

1 garlic clove, peeled and crushed

1 tsp cumin seeds

2 tbsp finely chopped fresh coriander

1 small egg yolk

salt and freshly ground black pepper

low calorie cooking spray

rocket or other salad leaves and lime wedges, to serve

for the mayo

4 level tbsp extra-light mayonnaise

1 tbsp quark

1 tbsp sweet chilli sauce

finely grated zest and juice of ½ lime

Place the sweet potato in a large saucepan and fill with just enough water to cover. Bring to the boil and cook until the potato is tender and easily pierced with a fork – about 10 minutes. Drain thoroughly, transfer to a mixing bowl and mash well.

Stir in the red chilli, spring onions, garlic, cumin seeds, coriander and egg yolk and season to taste.

When the mixture is cool enough, use your hands to form the potato mixture into six slightly flattened cakes, about 6cm in diameter, and spray with low calorie cooking spray. Place a large frying pan over a medium-high heat and cook the potato cakes, three at a time, for about 5-6 minutes until golden brown on each side, turning once.

Make the mayo by mixing all the ingredients together in a small bowl. Serve the sweet potato cakes on a bed of rocket or salad leaves with a dollop of the sweet chilli mayo and lime wedges to squeeze over.

warm puy lentil and goats' cheese salad

Enjoy the marriage of classic 'salt and pepper' flavours in this delicious vegetarian starter. Pairing peppery Puy lentils and tangy, salty goats' cheese will leave your guest in no doubt – you're a seasoned entertainer!

serves 2

each serving is:

4 Syns on Extra Easy

4 Syns on Green

10 Syns on Original

preparation time: 10 minutes

cooking time: 20 minutes

Toss the tomatoes, red onion, garlic, celery, lemon juice and French dressing in a bowl and leave to stand at room temperature.

Cook the lentils in a saucepan of boiling water for 20 minutes or until just tender, drain well and add to the bowl.

Crumble over the goats' cheese and scatter over the parsley. Season to taste and toss to mix well before serving.

100g cherry tomatoes, quartered

1 red onion, peeled, halved and very finely sliced

1 garlic clove, peeled and crushed

2 celery sticks, finely chopped

juice of 1 lemon

75ml fat free French dressing

75g Puy lentils

50g soft goats' cheese

a small bunch of roughly chopped flat-leaf parsley

salt and freshly ground black pepper

saltimbocca chicken
with a marsala jus

serves 2

each serving is:

2½ Syns on Extra Easy

12 Syns on Green

12 Syns on Original

preparation time: 25-30 minutes

cooking time: under 30 minutes

---

for the mash

500g potatoes, peeled
and roughly chopped

75ml hot vegetable stock

1 level tbsp grated
Parmesan cheese

a small handful of
finely chopped fresh basil

salt and freshly ground
black pepper

for the chicken

2 large skinless
chicken breast fillets

4 basil leaves

2 slices of prosciutto ham,
all visible fat removed

low calorie cooking spray

2 tbsp Marsala wine

150ml chicken stock

Saltimbocca translates as 'jumps into the mouth', and your tastebuds will be jumping for joy after enjoying this delicious medley of prosciutto ham, chicken, posh mashed potato and a Marsala sauce.

Boil the potatoes in lightly salted water for 15-20 minutes or until tender. Drain and mash well. Stir in the stock, then the Parmesan and basil. Season well, stir to combine and keep warm.

Preheat the oven to 200°C/Fan 180°C/Gas 6.

Meanwhile make a cut in each chicken breast and tuck two basil leaves into each fillet then wrap with a slice of prosciutto ham and secure with a cocktail stick.

Spray a large frying pan with low calorie cooking spray and add the chicken breasts. Cook over a medium heat for 2-3 minutes until golden, then remove the cocktail sticks, turn over and cook for 2 minutes more. Pour over the wine and allow to bubble for 1 minute. Add the stock and simmer for around 10 minutes or until the chicken is cooked through.

Lift the chicken out of the pan, cover to keep warm, then boil the pan juices to reduce a little. Serve with the basil mash and the pan juices spooned over.

Accompany with sautéed tenderstem broccoli, if you like.

rack of lamb
with a mustard crust

This eye-catching dish really does make entertaining effortless… although your guest will never know! Marinated overnight for maximum flavour and needing very little attention before serving, it's guaranteed to become your go-to entertaining entrée!

Place the garlic, rosemary, lemon zest and juice, mustard powder, tomato purée and yogurt into a bowl, season to taste and mix until well combined.

Using a small sharp knife, make deep cuts all over the flesh side of the lamb rack and place in a roasting tin lined with baking parchment.

Spread the mustard paste mixture all over the lamb, cover and leave to marinate for 8 hours or overnight if time permits.

Preheat the oven to 220°C/Fan 200°C/Gas 7.

Place the lamb on a non-stick baking tray, rib-side up, and roast in the oven for 20 minutes or until the lamb is cooked to your liking.

Remove the rack from the oven, cover with foil and leave to rest for 10 minutes.

Carve the rack into cutlets and serve.

serves 2

each serving is:

Free on Extra Easy

Free on Original

13½ **Syns** on Green

preparation time: 30 minutes plus overnight marinating

cooking time: under 20 minutes

---

4 garlic cloves, peeled and crushed

4 tbsp finely chopped fresh rosemary

finely grated zest and juice of 1 lemon

1 tsp English mustard powder

6 tbsp tomato purée

2 tbsp fat free natural yogurt

salt and freshly ground black pepper

1 French-trimmed rack of lamb (with 7-9 ribs)

For a more budget-friendly meal, you can swap the rack of lamb for four lean leg steaks. Grill for 5 minutes on each side or until cooked to your liking.

grilled
lobster tails

serves 2

each serving is:

Free on Extra Easy

Free on Original

6½ Syns on Green

preparation time: 25 minutes

cooking time: under 15 minutes

Take inspiration from 'under the sea' with this quick, easy and Free version of a gourmet dish. Teamed with Superfree 'spaghetti' made from ribbons of courgette, it's sure to make your dinner for two a truly memorable affair!

for the courgette 'spaghetti'

2 medium courgettes

salt and freshly ground black pepper

for the lobster

finely grated zest and juice of 1 lemon, plus extra zest to serve (optional)

4 tbsp fat free French dressing

1 red chilli, deseeded and finely chopped, plus extra to serve (optional)

2 garlic cloves, peeled and crushed

2 tbsp finely snipped fresh dill, plus extra to serve (optional)

4 lobster tails

First prepare the courgette spaghetti: slice the courgettes lengthways using a mandolin. Cut the slices into thin strips, like spaghetti, and put into a bowl. Season well and set aside until needed.

Preheat the grill to medium-high.

Place the lemon zest and juice in a bowl and add the fat free dressing, red chilli, garlic and dill. Season well and stir to combine.

Lay the lobster tails, flesh side up, on a cutting board. Using a large knife, cut the tails in half lengthways (use kitchen scissors to cut all the way through the shell if you need to).

Place the tails, cut side up, on a grill rack and brush with the lemon and garlic marinade.

Place the tails under the grill and cook for 10-12 minutes, basting frequently with the marinade. The lobster is ready when the shell turns red and the flesh is opaque and firm to the touch.

Meanwhile, bring a saucepan of water to the boil, add the courgette strips, cook for 1 minute and then drain thoroughly. Divide the courgette 'spaghetti' between two plates, add the lobster tails and scatter over chopped dill, lemon zest and red chilli, if you like.

Fresh lobster tails are available from the fishmonger or the fish counter at your local supermarket. You can also use frozen lobster tails. Thaw to room temperature by placing them in a sealed plastic bag and submerging them in a bowl of warm water.

summer
vegetable risotto

serves 2

each serving is:

Free on Extra Easy

Free on Green

13½ Syns on Original

preparation time: 10 minutes

cooking time: under 30 minutes

---

low calorie cooking spray

2 baby leeks, finely sliced

2 garlic cloves, peeled and finely chopped

200g asparagus tips, cut into 2cm lengths

6 baby carrots, trimmed and cut into thin matchsticks

150g risotto rice

650ml boiling hot vegetable stock

salt and freshly ground black pepper

finely grated zest of 1 lemon

Get fresh with this simple summery risotto. Ideal for entertaining or when you want a filling, tasty meal in a hurry, it's a great all-rounder. Add a delicate Parmesan 'crisp' for extra flair!

Spray a large pan with low calorie cooking spray and place over a medium heat. Add the leeks and garlic and stir-fry for 30 seconds. Add the asparagus, carrots and rice and stir-fry for 2-3 minutes.

Pour in half of the stock and leave to cook for 10 minutes, stirring often, until the liquid has been absorbed. Add the rest of the stock, then continue to stir and cook for a further 12-15 minutes until the rice is just tender and the liquid is absorbed but the mixture is still a bit saucy.

Season well then stir in the lemon zest.

Serve the risotto topped with the Parmesan 'crisps' (4½ Syns per serving), if using.

To make Parmesan 'crisps' for 2: line a baking sheet with baking parchment and coarsely grate 40g Parmesan cheese onto the parchment in a 10 x 15cm rectangle. Bake in a preheated oven at 180°C/Fan 160°C/Gas 4 for around 5 minutes until the cheese has melted and become golden. Remove from the oven and leave to cool completely. Break into shards when ready to serve.

spinach
and bacon medley

This delicious side dish is equally good as a light meal in its own right. Quick to make and packed with Superfree spinach, it'll make a strong addition to your meal for two!

Bring a large saucepan of lightly salted water to the boil, add the spinach and blanch for 1-2 minutes. Drain thoroughly.

Spray a large wok or frying pan with low calorie cooking spray and stir-fry the bacon for 2-3 minutes over a high heat until lightly golden.

Add the red pepper, onion and garlic and stir-fry over a high heat for 3-4 minutes.

Add the tomatoes, soy sauce, stock and chilli flakes, and stir-fry over a medium heat for 5-6 minutes until the vegetables are tender.

Stir in the spinach and toss to mix well.

Remove from the heat, check the seasoning and serve with a squeeze of lemon juice.

You can swap the spinach for kale if you prefer, although it will need a slightly longer cooking time.

serves 2

each serving is:

Free on Extra Easy

Free on Original

2 Syns on Green

preparation time: 15 minutes

cooking time: under 15 minutes

250g spinach leaves, tough stalks removed

low calorie cooking spray

50g lean back bacon, all visible fat removed, finely diced

½ red pepper, deseeded and finely diced

1 small onion, peeled, halved and thinly sliced

2 garlic cloves, peeled and crushed

2 tomatoes, deseeded and finely diced

1 tbsp light soy sauce

50ml vegetable stock

¼ tsp dried red chilli flakes

salt and freshly ground black pepper

a squeeze of lemon juice

pear and
dolcelatte salad

Sweet, salty and peppery, this lively side dish makes a delicious light lunch too. Dolcelatte translates as 'sweet milk', and the sweetness of the blue-veined cheese, ripe pears and syrupy balsamic dressing transform this dish from the ordinary to magnificentissimo!

serves 2

each serving is:

5 Syns on Extra Easy

5 Syns on Original

9 Syns on Green

preparation time: 10 minutes

cooking time: under 5 minutes

for the vinaigrette

4 tbsp balsamic vinegar

1 level tsp Dijon mustard

100ml fat free French dressing

¼ tsp dried thyme

1 clove garlic, peeled and crushed

salt and freshly ground
black pepper

for the salad

4 rashers lean bacon,
all visible fat removed

1 ripe pear

50g wild rocket leaves

1 medium beetroot, cooked,
peeled and cut into thin
batons/matchsticks

50g dolcelatte or a creamy blue
cheese, cut into small pieces

First make the vinaigrette by putting all the ingredients in a clean screw-top jar. Season and shake to combine.

Place the bacon under a preheated medium-hot grill and cook for 3-4 minutes or until crisp. Cut into bite-sized strips and set aside.

Halve the pear, remove the core and thinly slice lengthways.

Divide the rocket between two serving plates. Arrange the beetroot and pears over the leaves then scatter over the cheese and bacon.

Drizzle the vinaigrette over the salad and toss to mix well before serving.

*This **salad** can be served as*
*a **starter** or **side dish**.*

boulangère potato stacks

Transform the humble spud into an impressive boulangère tower. Cooked in little muffin tins, these stacks make a delicious accompaniment to any meat, chicken or fish dish.

serves 2

each serving is:

2 Syns on Extra Easy

2 Syns on Green

9½ Syns on Original

preparation time: 20 minutes

cooking time: under 45 minutes

400g Desirée potatoes

1 litre vegetable stock

low calorie cooking spray

4 tbsp finely chopped fresh flat-leaf parsley, plus extra to serve

4 tbsp quark

2 garlic cloves, peeled and crushed

salt and freshly ground black pepper

25g reduced fat Cheddar cheese, grated

Peel and slice the potatoes very thinly, using a mandolin if you have one.

Bring the stock to the boil in a large saucepan, add the potatoes and bring back to the boil.

Cook for 5 minutes then drain thoroughly, reserving the stock. Transfer the potatoes to a mixing bowl.

Preheat the oven to 200°C/Fan 180°C/Gas 6.

Lightly spray the insides of four deep non-stick muffin tins or chefs' rings with low calorie cooking spray.

In a small bowl, mix 6 tablespoons of the reserved stock with the chopped parsley, quark and garlic. Season well, pour this mixture over the potato slices and toss gently to combine.

Layer the coated potato slices into the muffin tins, pressing down to compact the mixture.

Scatter the grated cheese over the potato slices and place in the oven for 25-30 minutes until the tops are lightly browned.

Remove from the oven and run a small palette knife around the insides of each tin and carefully turn out onto serving plates. Scatter with chopped parsley to serve.

chocolate-dipped
strawberries

serves 2

each serving is:

5½ **Syns** on Extra Easy

5½ **Syns** on Green

5½ **Syns** on Original

preparation time: 10 minutes

cooking time: under 10 minutes

20g each of dark and white chocolate, broken into small pieces

12 large strawberries

The ultimate romantic dessert or petit four, chocolate-dipped strawberries are also a Food Optimiser's delight. For around 1 Syn per strawberry you can enjoy the crack of the set chocolate then the juicy, sweet soft fruit – delicious!

Place the dark chocolate and white chocolate in separate heatproof bowls, and place over two saucepans of gently simmering water.

When melted, dip the pointed end of each strawberry into one of the bowls of melted chocolate, transfer to a sheet of baking parchment and leave to set.

These strawberries are delicious dusted with a little icing sugar (1 Syn per level teaspoon).

prosecco and raspberry hearts

serves 2

each serving is:

2 Syns on Extra Easy

2 Syns on Green

2 Syns on Original

preparation time: 10 minutes plus overnight chilling

cooking time: none

---

2 tbsp sweetener

a few drops of raspberry or strawberry flavouring

2 sheets of leaf gelatine

100g raspberries

100ml Prosecco or sparkling white or rosé wine

fat free natural fromage frais and mint sprigs, to serve

Display your love… for food with this sophisticated dessert. Strictly for adults, these elegant jellies are made with Italian Prosecco to end your dinner for two with sparkle!

Pour 200ml of water into a saucepan and add the sweetener. Heat gently until the sweetener has completely dissolved, then stir in the flavouring.

Soak the gelatine in a bowl of cold water for 10 minutes. When soft, squeeze the excess water from the gelatine and stir into the syrup until it has completely dissolved.

Divide the raspberries between two 250ml heart-shaped moulds or stemmed glasses.

Pour the Prosecco or wine into the gelatine mixture, stir to mix well and pour over the raspberries.

Chill overnight then turn out on to serving plates (if using moulds) and serve with a spoonful of fromage frais, a sprig of mint and a dusting of icing sugar (1 Syn per level teaspoon).

*Alcohol sets more softly than other liquids.
To make sure your **jelly hearts** keep their shape,
make them a day ahead, then serve them
straight from the fridge.*

casual saturday with friends

Time spent with friends is precious — and laughter and good food should always be on the menu. To make sure no one has to slave away in the kitchen and miss out on all the fun, here are some simple dishes to keep casual gatherings… well, casual.

mackerel fishcakes
with chunky tomato mayo

Bring the best of bistro dining to your dinner table with these flavour-packed fishcakes. These work well served as a starter or as a main course accompanied with a mixed salad.

Cook the potatoes in a large saucepan of lightly salted boiling water for around 15 minutes until the potatoes are just tender. Drain thoroughly, return to the pan and mash until fairly smooth. Allow to cool completely.

Meanwhile, in another saucepan, cook the cabbage in boiling water for 3-4 minutes. Drain thoroughly and squeeze out any excess liquid. Allow to cool.

Put the mashed potato and drained cabbage into a wide mixing bowl with the spring onions, horseradish, egg, tarragon, lemon zest and mackerel. Mix well, season and shape into 12 cakes, then cover and chill for a minimum of 6 hours or overnight if time permits.

When ready to cook, preheat the oven to 200°C/Fan 180°C/Gas 6. Place the cakes on a baking sheet, spray with low calorie cooking spray and cook in the oven for 20-25 minutes or until lightly golden.

While the cakes are cooking, place all the mayo ingredients in a bowl and stir to combine.

Remove the cakes from the oven and serve warm or at room temperature with the chunky mayo, a watercress salad and lemon wedges to squeeze over.

makes 12 fishcakes

each fishcake is:

1 Syn on Extra Easy

3 Syns on Original

7 Syns on Green

preparation time: 30 minutes plus chilling

cooking time: 35-40 minutes

for the fishcakes

600g Desirée potatoes, peeled and roughly chopped

200g green cabbage, very finely shredded

8 spring onions, very finely chopped

1 tsp grated horseradish

1 egg, lightly beaten

3 tbsp freshly chopped tarragon

finely grated zest of 1 large lemon

500g peppered smoked mackerel fillets, skinned and roughly flaked

salt and freshly ground black pepper

low calorie cooking spray

watercress salad and lemon wedges, to serve

for the mayo

4 plum tomatoes, deseeded and roughly chopped

100g gherkins, roughly chopped

a small handful of freshly chopped parsley

100g fat free natural fromage frais

4 level tbsp extra light mayonnaise

rustic garlic chicken tray bake

serves 6

each serving is:

Free on Extra Easy

4 Syns on Original

11 Syns on Green

preparation time: 30 minutes

cooking time: 1 hour 40 minutes

---

low calorie cooking spray

salt and freshly ground
black pepper

12 large skinless chicken thighs

600g Desirée potatoes, peeled
and cut into 2.5mm thick slices

800g medium vine tomatoes,
halved

2 courgettes, thickly sliced

3 large onions, peeled
and thickly sliced

4 garlic cloves, peeled
and finely chopped

4-5 small rosemary sprigs

4 tbsp finely chopped fresh parsley

1 tsp dried red chilli flakes

finely grated zest and
juice of 1 lemon

250ml chicken stock

This is a really easy meal to cook for friends. You can put it all together before everyone arrives and simply pop it in the oven – giving you time to get ready while the delicious aromas of Mediterranean cuisine fill the kitchen.

Preheat the oven to 180°C/Fan 160°C/Gas 4. Spray a large frying pan with low calorie cooking spray and place over a high heat. Season the chicken thighs, add to the pan and cook for 2-3 minutes on each side. Remove with a slotted spoon and set aside.

Spray the potatoes with low calorie cooking spray and add to the pan in a single layer. Cook for around 5 minutes on each side until lightly browned. Remove from the heat.

Spray a medium roasting tray with low calorie cooking spray and layer the base with the tomatoes, courgettes, onions and potatoes.

Place the chicken on top of the vegetables in a single layer and sprinkle over the garlic, herbs, chilli flakes and the lemon zest and juice.

Pour the stock over the chicken and vegetables, cover with foil and bake in the oven for 1½ hours until the potatoes are soft and the chicken is tender, removing the foil for the last 10 minutes of cooking. Bring the tray to the table and let everyone help themselves.

chilli beef and vegetable pie

serves 6

each serving is:

Free on Extra Easy

Free on Original

8½ Syns on Green

preparation time: 25 minutes

cooking time: about 1 hour

---

low calorie cooking spray

800g extra lean minced beef

1 large onion, peeled
and finely chopped

2 garlic cloves, peeled and crushed

1 red chilli, deseeded
and finely chopped

2 tbsp mild curry powder

2 red peppers, deseeded
and cut into 1.5cm dice

300g green beans, trimmed
and cut into 1.5cm lengths

1 large carrot, peeled
and cut into 1.5cm dice

200g passata

6 tbsp tomato purée

400g fat free natural yogurt

4 large eggs

a large handful of finely
chopped fresh coriander

salt and freshly ground
black pepper

mixed leaf and tomato salad,
to serve

This comforting pie is a tasty twist on classic beef chilli and a sure-fire way to spice up your Saturday nights – spoon at the ready!

Preheat the oven to 180°C/Fan 160°C/Gas 4. Spray a large frying pan with low calorie cooking spray and place over a medium heat. Add the minced beef and stir-fry for around 3 minutes, stirring constantly, until the meat changes colour.

Add the onion and cook for 5 minutes, stirring occasionally, until the onion starts to soften and the mince is lightly browned.

Add the garlic, red chilli, curry powder, red peppers, green beans and carrot and stir-fry for 3-4 minutes. Remove the pan from the heat and stir in the passata and tomato purée.

Spoon the mixture into a 2-litre shallow ovenproof dish and press down well with the back of a spoon.

Whisk the yogurt with the eggs, stir in the chopped coriander and season well with salt and pepper. Pour over the beef mixture to cover evenly.

Cook in the oven for around 50 minutes until the mixture is piping hot and the top is set and golden brown. Serve immediately with a mixed leaf and tomato salad.

serves 6

each serving is:

Free on Extra Easy

10 Syns on Green

14½ Syns on Original

preparation time: 30 minutes plus marinating

cooking time: about 1½ hours

for the lamb

4 garlic cloves, peeled and crushed

1.5cm piece root ginger, peeled and finely grated

150g fat free natural yogurt, plus extra sprinkled with paprika to serve

6 tbsp finely chopped fresh coriander, plus extra to serve

800g lean lamb leg steaks, all visible fat removed, cut into bite-size pieces

salt and freshly ground black pepper

low calorie cooking spray

1 onion, peeled and finely chopped

1 tbsp ground coriander

2 tsp each of ground cumin and ground cinnamon

400g can chopped tomatoes

400g spinach leaves, chopped

for the rice

1 tbsp cumin seeds

1 onion, peeled, halved and thinly sliced

6 cloves

6 green cardamom pods, lightly crushed

1 cinnamon stick

500g basmati rice

1.2 litres vegetable stock

2 tsp saffron threads

¼ tsp ground turmeric

layered lamb and spinach pilaf

Keep the washing-up to a minimum with this simple one-pot lamb and spinach pilaf. This Middle Eastern-inspired dish is perfect for sharing with friends and family.

Prepare the lamb marinade by mixing the garlic, ginger, yogurt and chopped coriander in a bowl. Add the lamb and toss to coat evenly. Season to taste, cover and leave to marinate in the fridge for 6 hours, or overnight if time permits.

Spray a heavy-based saucepan with low calorie cooking spray, add the onion and cook over a medium-low heat for around 15 minutes until lightly golden.

Add the marinated lamb and cook over a high heat for 2-3 minutes, stirring often. Stir in the ground spices, tomatoes and spinach, season well and bring to the boil. Reduce the heat to low and simmer gently, uncovered, for around 20 minutes or until the lamb is tender and most of the mixture has thickened. Set aside.

Meanwhile, make the rice by spraying another heavy-based pan with low calorie cooking spray. Add the cumin seeds, onion, cloves, cardamom pods and cinnamon stick and stir-fry for 2-3 minutes. Stir in the rice and stir-fry for 2 minutes. Pour in the stock, bring to the boil, cover and simmer gently for 7-8 minutes until cooked through. Remove from the heat and drain well.

In a bowl, mix the saffron threads and turmeric together with 6 tablespoons of hot water and set aside.

Preheat the oven to 180°C/Fan 160°C/Gas 4. Lightly spray a lidded, medium ovenproof casserole dish with low calorie cooking spray.

Spread a thin layer of the lamb mixture over the base and cover evenly with half of the rice. Top with the remaining lamb mixture and cover with the remaining rice. Drizzle over the saffron mixture, cover the dish with foil and top with the lid.

Bake in the oven for 30 minutes. Remove from the oven and allow to rest, still covered, for around 20 minutes. Scatter with the remaining coriander and serve with the paprika-sprinkled yogurt.

italian aubergine, basil and tomato bake

Sink your serving spoon into this impressive but simple Italian main course that's bursting with sunshine colours and flavours. Your guests will be delighted (and they'll never guess it's so healthy!)

serves 6

each serving is:

4 Syns on Extra Easy

4 Syns on Green

4 Syns on Original

preparation time: 20 minutes

cooking time: about 1 hour

Preheat the oven to 180°C/Fan 160°C/Gas 4.

Spray a frying pan with low calorie cooking spray, add the garlic and gently stir-fry for 1-2 minutes.

Add the tomatoes, sweetener, chilli flakes, dried herbs and cinnamon stick and simmer for 20-25 minutes until thickened. Season well.

Meanwhile, spray the aubergine slices lightly on both sides with low calorie cooking spray, season and cook on a preheated ridged griddle, in batches, turning a few times until completely tender (you could also do this in a frying pan). It's important to get the aubergine as tender as possible, so give it time.

Remove the cinnamon stick from the frying pan and put a few spoonfuls of the sauce in the bottom of a large ovenproof dish. Cover with one-third of the aubergine slices and half of the basil leaves then repeat, finishing with a layer of aubergine.

Spoon a thin layer of sauce over the aubergine, sprinkle with the Parmesan and bake for 30-40 minutes until bubbling and golden. Serve warm or at room temperature.

low calorie cooking spray

4 garlic cloves, peeled and thinly sliced

2 x 400g cans chopped tomatoes

¼ tsp sweetener

1 tsp dried red chilli flakes

1 tsp dried mixed Italian herbs

1 cinnamon stick

salt and freshly ground black pepper

4 large aubergines, cut into 1.5cm thick slices

2 large handfuls of basil leaves

120g Parmesan cheese, grated

sautéed green beans
with shallots and cherry tomatoes

serves 6

each serving is:

Free on Extra Easy

Free on Green

Free on Original

preparation time: 20 minutes

cooking time: under 12 minutes

600g green beans, trimmed

low calorie cooking spray

4 shallots, peeled and
very finely chopped

400g mixed cherry tomatoes,
halved or quartered

4 garlic cloves, peeled
and finely chopped

salt and freshly ground
black pepper

2 tbsp balsamic vinegar

These balsamic-glazed green beans are packed with crunch and make a superb Superfree side dish – perfect for fuss-free weekend entertaining and ready in less than 20 minutes.

Place the green beans in a large saucepan, fill with enough water to cover and bring to the boil over a high heat. Reduce the heat to medium-low and simmer for 5 minutes. Drain and set aside.

Meanwhile, spray a large frying pan with low calorie cooking spray and add the shallots, cherry tomatoes and garlic and stir-fry for 3-4 minutes over a medium-low heat.

Add the green beans to the frying pan, turn the heat to high and sauté for 3-4 minutes or until piping hot.

Remove from the heat, season to taste and drizzle over the balsamic vinegar. Toss to mix well and serve warm or at room temperature.

beetroot bistro salad

serves 6

each serving is:

2 Syns on Extra Easy

2 Syns on Green

3½ **Syns** on Original

preparation time: 25 minutes

cooking time: under 20 minutes

250g frozen broad beans

low calorie cooking spray

1 red onion, peeled,
halved and thinly sliced

2 garlic cloves, peeled and sliced

1 tbsp freshly chopped thyme

700g cooked beetroot, peeled
and cut into thin matchsticks

140g bag mixed salad leaves

75g feta cheese, cut into small
bite-sized cubes

for the dressing

150ml fat free vinaigrette

½ tsp runny honey

1 level tsp wholegrain mustard

salt and freshly ground
black pepper

The contrasting flavours and textures of beetroot, broad beans and red onion make this a decadent dinner party salad. Drizzled with a honey-mustard dressing and crumbled feta cheese it really adds the wow factor – guaranteed!

Cook the broad beans according to the packet instructions, then drain and refresh in cold water. Peel the skins off the beans with your fingers – this is a fiddly job, but worth the effort.

Spray a large frying pan with low calorie cooking spray, add the onion and garlic and stir-fry for 1-2 minutes over a medium heat until a pale golden colour.

Stir in the chopped thyme, then add the beetroot and stir-fry gently for 3-4 minutes, so the flavours mingle. Remove from the heat and leave to cool.

Transfer the beetroot mixture to a wide salad bowl and add the salad leaves.

Mix the vinaigrette, honey and mustard together and season well. Pour over the beetroot mixture and toss gently to mix through.

Just before serving, toss in the broad beans and feta cubes.

spiced paprika
warm potato salad

Potato salad is a picnic food favourite but our luxury version has been given a delicious dinner party make-over with chopped apples, cucumber and a fiery paprika dressing. Your guests will be begging for the recipe!

Boil the potatoes in a large saucepan of lightly salted water for 15 minutes until tender. Drain well, set aside and keep warm.

Mix all the dressing ingredients together, season with salt and set aside.

To make the salad, core the apples and cut the flesh into 1.5cm cubes. Place in a bowl with the potatoes and cucumber, then drizzle over the dressing.

Toss in the chopped herbs, mix well and serve warm or at room temperature.

serves 6

each serving is:

Free on Extra Easy

Free on Green

6½ Syns on Original

preparation time: 25 minutes

cooking time: under 15 minutes

6 Maris Piper potatoes, peeled and cut into 1.5cm cubes

3 red dessert apples

1 cucumber, cut into 1.5cm cubes

a large handful each of chopped coriander and mint

for the dressing

1 tbsp freshly ground black pepper

1 tbsp dry-roasted cumin seeds, roughly ground

¼ tsp ground turmeric

1 tsp nigella seeds (black onion seeds)

1 tsp smoked paprika

¼ tsp sweetener

125ml fat free vinaigrette

juice of 2 limes

salt

baked american blueberry and orange cheesecake

serves 8

each serving is:

8½ Syns on Extra Easy

8½ Syns on Green

8½ Syns on Original

preparation time: 20 minutes plus chilling

cooking time: under 1 hour

---

12 reduced fat digestive biscuits, finely crushed

6 level tbsp low fat spread

500g quark

3 large eggs

1 tsp ground cinnamon

2 tsp vanilla essence

6 tbsp sweetener

finely grated zest of 1 orange

500g blueberries

200g fat free natural fromage frais

orange zest, to decorate

icing sugar, to dust (optional)

For a Saturday afternoon treat, serve a slice of this baked cheesecake that's bursting with blueberries and zesty orange. This fab, fruity dessert is sure to leave a sweet taste on everyone's lips – and a smile in their hearts!

Place the crushed biscuits in a bowl and melt the low fat spread. Add to the biscuits and stir to mix well. Spoon into a 22cm non-stick, springform cake tin, pressing down firmly to make a smooth and even base. Chill to firm up.

Preheat the oven to 160°C/Fan 140°C/Gas 3.

Beat the quark, eggs, ground cinnamon, vanilla essence, sweetener and the orange zest together until well combined.

Fold in half of the blueberries and pour over the prepared biscuit base. Place in the oven and cook for 50-55 minutes or until just set and golden.

Remove from the oven and leave to cool completely. Cover with cling film and chill in the fridge for at least 6 hours or overnight if time permits.

Spread the fromage frais over the top and scatter the remaining blueberries. Decorate with grated orange zest, dust with the icing sugar (1 Syn per level teaspoon), if using, and cut into wedges to serve.

orange and lime jelly pots

A match made in dessert heaven – orange segments set in a lemon and lime jelly, topped with a creamy layer of custard and sprinkle of cocoa. This irresistible pudding proves that jelly isn't just for kids!

Make the jelly according to the packet instructions and allow to cool.

Divide the orange segments between six dessert bowls or glasses, reserving a few segments for decoration.

Pour the cooled jelly mixture over the segments and chill in the fridge for at least 6 hours or until set.

Spoon the custard over the set jellies and top with the fromage frais.

Decorate with the reserved orange segments and lightly dust with cocoa powder before serving.

makes 6

each jelly is:

4½ **Syns** on Extra Easy

4½ **Syns** on Green

4½ **Syns** on Original

preparation time: 15 minutes plus chilling

cooking time: none

2 x 11.5g sachets sugar free lemon and lime jelly crystals

4 large oranges, peeled and segmented

600g low fat custard

400g fat free natural fromage frais

1 level tsp cocoa powder, to dust

posh sunday lunch

Sunday lunch is a time to enjoy a filling feast with family or friends before the working week begins again. All these dishes taste divine and, because they're relatively easy to make, you'll be able to provide the wow factor – without the 'ow' factor!

herbed cheese and bacon soufflés

serves 6

each serving is:

3½ Syns on Extra Easy

3½ Syns on Original

4½ Syns on Green

preparation time: 20 minutes

cooking time: 20 minutes

low calorie cooking spray

100g lean bacon, all visible fat removed, cut into 1.5cm pieces

1 red chilli, deseeded and finely chopped

8 spring onions, finely chopped

6 eggs, separated

6 tbsp each of finely chopped fresh chives and dill

100g Parmesan cheese, finely grated

¼ tsp English mustard powder

salt and freshly ground black pepper

mixed salad leaves, to serve

These show-stopper soufflés are just perfect as a Sunday lunch starter. They're light and fluffy with a delicious cheese-filled centre, and your guests will never believe the cloud-like creaminess is slimming-friendly!

Preheat the oven to 180°C/Fan 160°C/Gas 4.

Prepare a bain-marie by placing a roasting pan one-third-full of warm water into the oven.

Lightly spray the insides of six individual ramekins or one medium soufflé dish with low calorie cooking spray.

Spray a frying pan with low calorie cooking spray and stir-fry the bacon, red chilli and spring onions for 6-8 minutes, then drain thoroughly in a metal sieve to get rid of any excess moisture and pat dry with kitchen paper.

Meanwhile put the egg whites into a bowl and whisk until just stiff. In a separate bowl, beat the egg yolks and add the bacon and spring onion mixture, chopped herbs and three-quarters of the cheese. Season with the mustard powder and some salt and pepper.

Using a metal spoon, fold the egg whites into the egg yolk and bacon mixture. Spoon this into the ramekins, almost to the top, and sprinkle over the remaining cheese.

Place in the bain-marie and cook for around 20 minutes until risen and lightly set. Serve with a few mixed salad leaves.

These soufflés can be made in advance and heated up the next day. When you're ready to serve, preheat the oven to 200°C/Fan 180°C/Gas 6 and cook for about 5 minutes or until warmed through.

chicken liver parfait
with red onion marmalade

serves 6

each serving is:

2½ Syns on Extra Easy

2½ Syns on Original

6 Syns on Green

preparation time: 30 minutes plus overnight chilling

cooking time: under 1 hour

for the parfait

400g chicken livers, trimmed

low calorie cooking spray

2 shallots, peeled and finely diced

50ml chicken stock

2 garlic cloves, peeled and crushed

1 tbsp fresh thyme leaves

1 tbsp brandy

2 large eggs

200g quark

salt and freshly ground black pepper

6 small bay leaves, to garnish

1 tbsp pink peppercorns, crushed, to garnish

4 slices wholemeal bread (from a small 400g loaf), toasted, to serve

for the red onion marmalade

4 red onions, peeled, halved and thickly sliced

300ml chicken stock

4 tbsp balsamic vinegar

2 tbsp sweetener

The word 'parfait' means 'perfect' and that's exactly what this wonderfully smooth starter is. Served with tangy red onion marmalade to cut through the richness, it's a divinely delicious dish.

Preheat the oven to 160°C/Fan 140°C/Gas 3.

Prepare a bain-marie by placing a roasting pan one-third-full of warm water into the oven.

Rinse the chicken livers under cold running water and pat dry with kitchen paper.

Spray a large frying pan with low calorie cooking spray, add the livers and cook over a high heat for 2-3 minutes, until sealed on the outside but still pink on the inside. Remove from the pan and leave to cool.

Place the shallots, stock, garlic, thyme and brandy in a small saucepan. Bring to the boil then simmer briskly until reduced and almost syrupy. Remove from the heat.

Place the cooled livers into a food processor along with the eggs, the shallot sauce and the quark. Blend to a smooth purée, season well and spoon into six ramekins.

Place foil over each ramekin, remove the bain-marie from the oven and carefully add the ramekins. Bake for 30 minutes.

Remove from the oven and leave to cool completely before chilling overnight in the fridge.

Make the red onion marmalade by placing the onions in a saucepan with the stock, balsamic vinegar and sweetener. Bring to the boil, reduce the heat to low and cook for 20-25 minutes until tender. Drain in a sieve and set aside.

Garnish the parfaits with fresh bay leaves and pink peppercorns and serve with the red onion marmalade and wholemeal toast.

leek and cannellini bean soup

serves 6

each serving is:

Free on Extra Easy

Free on Green

7 Syns on Original

preparation time: 20 minutes

cooking time: about 45 minutes

---

low calorie cooking spray

3 leeks, thinly sliced

2 garlic cloves, peeled
and roughly chopped

500g King Edward potatoes,
peeled and roughly diced

2 x 400g cans cannellini beans,
drained and rinsed

1.5 litres vegetable stock

a small handful of very finely
chopped fresh flat-leaf parsley,
plus extra sprigs to garnish

salt and freshly ground
black pepper

6 tbsp fat free natural fromage frais

The leek and beans combine beautifully in this sumptuous soup – and because you can prepare it in advance, it's the perfect opener to an elaborate meal.

Spray a large saucepan with low calorie cooking spray and place over a medium heat. Cook the leeks and garlic for 5 minutes until softened.

Add the potatoes, cannellini beans and stock, bring to the boil then cover and simmer gently for 35-40 minutes until the vegetables are very tender. Using a hand-held blender, purée the soup in the pan until smooth.

Stir in the parsley and season to taste before ladling into six shallow soup plates or bowls.

Top each bowl with a tablespoon of fromage frais and serve warm, garnished with parsley sprigs.

*Drizzle each serving with 1 teaspoon of **truffle-infused olive oil** for a taste of luxury (2 Syns per teaspoon).*

poached salmon
with champagne sauce

This salmon dish makes a beautifully elegant main course for entertaining – and the caviar adds a really special touch. Enjoy with a glass of bubbly for an indulgent Sunday lunch!

Lightly spray a large frying pan with low calorie cooking spray and add the salmon fillets in a single layer to fit snugly.

Pour the Champagne or wine and stock over the fish and bring it to a simmer over a medium heat. Cover and gently poach for 8-10 minutes or until just cooked through.

Meanwhile, spray a saucepan with low calorie cooking spray and add the shallots, carrot, celery and garlic. Stir and cook over a medium-low heat for 6-8 minutes.

Carefully lift the poached salmon fillets out of the pan and transfer to a warmed dish. Cover with foil and keep warm.

Strain the poaching liquid through a fine mesh sieve and add the liquid to the shallot mixture in the saucepan.

Bring to the boil and add the cornflour mixture and chopped dill. Bring back to the boil and cook until slightly thickened, stirring continuously.

Serve the salmon with the sauce spooned over. For a really special touch, top with salmon roe (½ Syn per 2 teaspoons on Green), and a sprig of dill. This is delicious served with a green salad or a selection of green vegetables.

serves 6

each serving is:

1 Syn on Extra Easy

1 Syn on Original

16½ Syns on Green

preparation time: 20 minutes

cooking time: under 30 minutes

---

low calorie cooking spray

6 large middle-cut, skinless salmon fillets

100ml Champagne or sparkling white wine

400ml vegetable stock

2 shallots, peeled and very finely diced

1 carrot, peeled and very finely diced

2 celery sticks, very finely diced

2 garlic cloves, peeled and crushed

2 level tsp cornflour mixed with 2 tsp water

2 tbsp very finely chopped dill, plus extra sprigs to garnish

salmon roe/caviar, to serve (optional)

mixed peppercorn crusted beef
with cabbage and horseradish cream

serves 6

each serving is:

½ **Syn** on Extra Easy

½ **Syn** on Original

15 Syns on Green

preparation time: 25 minutes

cooking time: under 30 minutes

---

6 large, thick, lean fillet steaks, all visible fat removed

salt

3 tbsp mixed crushed peppercorns

low calorie cooking spray

1 tbsp freshly chopped rosemary

1 garlic clove, peeled and crushed

1 small onion, peeled, halved and sliced

600g Savoy cabbage, shredded

200ml beef stock

1 level tbsp creamed horseradish

4 tbsp fat free natural fromage frais

1 level tbsp low fat soft cheese

1 tbsp roughly chopped fresh parsley

If you're a steak fan you'll love this luxurious dish that's just right for special occasions. Succulent fillet steak is accompanied by a delicious creamy cabbage – heaven!

Season the steaks well with salt and the crushed peppercorns.

Spray a large frying pan with low calorie cooking spray and place over a high heat.

Add the steaks in a single layer and cook for 3-4 minutes on each side or until cooked to your liking. Remove the steaks with a slotted spoon, transfer to a warmed plate, cover and keep warm.

Wipe the frying pan with kitchen paper and re-spray with low calorie cooking spray.

Place over a high heat and add the rosemary, garlic, onion and cabbage. Stir-fry for 4-5 minutes, then add the stock and season well. Cook over a high heat for 4-5 minutes until the cabbage is just tender.

Remove from the heat and stir in the horseradish cream, fromage frais and soft cheese.

Divide the cabbage between six plates, top with the peppered steaks, scatter over the parsley and serve immediately.

roast tarragon and mustard chicken

These flavour-packed parcels of chicken make an elegant main course that's sure to become a Sunday staple. Because they can be prepared ahead of time, they'll look after themselves while you catch up on the weekend's papers!

Preheat the oven to 200°C/Fan 180°C/Gas 6.

In a bowl, mix the cottage cheese, garlic, tarragon, lemon zest and mustard together. Season well.

Make a cut in the side of each chicken breast and stuff with the mustard mixture. Wrap each stuffed breast with two bacon rashers – not too tightly, but enough to hold the chicken together.

Season to taste, place on a baking sheet lined with baking parchment and drizzle over the lemon juice.

Roast in the oven for 20-25 minutes until cooked through. Serve immediately.

Pancetta works well in place of the bacon, just add 2 Syns per serving on on Extra Easy and Original, if using.

serves 6

each serving is:

Free on Extra Easy

Free on Original

12 Syns on Green

preparation time: 15 minutes

cooking time: under 30 minutes

100g low fat natural cottage cheese

2 garlic cloves, peeled and crushed

4 tbsp finely chopped fresh tarragon

finely grated zest and juice of 1 lemon

1 level tbsp wholegrain mustard

salt and freshly ground black pepper

6 large skinless and boneless chicken breasts

12 lean bacon rashers, all visible fat removed

stuffed spinach and mushroom crêpes

makes 12 crêpes

each crêpe is:

½ **Syn** on Extra Easy

½ **Syn** on Green

½ **Syn** on Original

preparation time: 25 minutes

cooking time: under 40 minutes

For an impressive vegetarian main course you can't beat these creamy crêpes. Soft, herby, juicy pancakes are filled with mushrooms, tomatoes and spinach to deliver a flavour-packed meal.

for the crêpes

10 large eggs

6 tbsp finely chopped mixed herbs of your choice (eg chives, parsley and tarragon)

salt and freshly ground black pepper

for the filling

low calorie cooking spray

500g baby button mushrooms, halved

3 garlic cloves, peeled and crushed

½ tsp cumin seeds

10 spring onions, finely sliced

400g baby spinach leaves

200g cherry tomatoes, halved or quartered

200g quark

4 level tbsp low fat soft cheese

fresh chives, to garnish

Crack the eggs into a large bowl, add the chopped herbs and 2 tablespoons of water and season to taste. Beat gently to break up the eggs, pour into a large measuring jug and set aside while preparing the filling.

Spray a large saucepan with low calorie cooking spray and place over a high heat. Add the mushrooms, garlic, cumin seeds and spring onions and cook for around 5 minutes until the mushrooms have softened and the mushroom juices have evaporated.

Add the spinach and stir-fry for 4-5 minutes or until wilted. Add the tomatoes and stir-fry over a high heat for 1-2 minutes. Remove from the heat and stir in the quark and soft cheese. Set aside and keep warm.

Spray an 18cm frying pan with low calorie cooking spray and place over a high heat for a few seconds until hot. Pour in one-twelfth of the egg and herb mixture. Cook for about 1 minute, stirring gently with a wooden spatula and pulling the cooked egg from the edge towards the centre to let the liquid egg flow on to the pan.

When the crêpe holds together, stop stirring and cook for 30 seconds or until the underside is golden brown and the top is just setting.

Spoon one-twelfth of the mushroom mixture along the middle third of the crêpe and fold both sides over the top.

Quickly slide the folded crêpe on to a warmed plate and keep warm then repeat until you have 12 stuffed crêpes.

Garnish with the chives and serve with a green salad.

petits pois
à la française

Transform the humble pea into a striking side dish in just 30 minutes. With tasty bacon, softened lettuce and onions, it really is a flavour combination you won't want to miss.

serves 6

each serving is:

Free on Extra Easy

2½ Syns on Green

2½ Syns on Original

preparation time: 10 minutes

cooking time: under 20 minutes

---

low calorie cooking spray

2 onions, peeled, halved and thinly sliced

200g lean back bacon, all visible fat removed, cut into thin strips

4 little gem lettuces, roughly shredded

150ml chicken stock

500g frozen petits pois

salt and freshly ground black pepper

Spray a heavy-based saucepan with low calorie cooking spray and place over a medium-low heat.

Add the onion and bacon and cook for 10-12 minutes or until the onion is really soft.

Add the lettuce and cook for 2 minutes.

Add the stock, bring to a simmer then add the peas and cook for 5 minutes until cooked through.

Season and serve.

traditional roast veg
with **rosemary** and **thyme**

Roasting these lovely baby vegetables brings out their natural sweetness and intensifies the taste. The fresh herbs and vinaigrette add extra depth to the flavour and makes them a Sunday lunch essential.

Preheat the oven to 200°C/Fan 180°C/Gas 6.

Lightly spray a large roasting tray with low calorie cooking spray, brush it with a little of the vinaigrette and add all the vegetables.

Season them well, add the herb sprigs and the bay leaf, then spoon the remaining vinaigrette over and toss all the vegetables around so they get a good coating. Cover tightly with foil.

Place the tray on the middle shelf of the oven and cook for around 1 hour until the veg is cooked through. Transfer the vegetables into a serving dish and garnish with sprigs of thyme.

serves 6

each serving is:

Free on Extra Easy

Free on Green

4½ Syns on Original

❄ Ⓥ

preparation time: 20 minutes

cooking time: 45 minutes

---

low calorie cooking spray

6 tbsp fat free vinaigrette

400g baby carrots,
trimmed and quartered

400g baby parsnips,
trimmed and quartered

350g small red potatoes, unpeeled
and each cut into 8 wedges

2 medium onions, peeled
and cut into 12 wedges

6 celery sticks,
cut into 3cm lengths

salt and freshly ground
black pepper

3 fresh thyme sprigs,
plus extra to garnish

2 fresh rosemary sprigs

1 bay leaf

duchess potatoes

serves 6

each serving is:

Free on Extra Easy

Free on Green

6½ Syns on Original

preparation time: 25 minutes

cooking time: under 1 hour

1kg Desirée potatoes, peeled and roughly chopped

a pinch of grated nutmeg

2 garlic cloves, peeled and crushed

1 tbsp finely chopped fresh rosemary, plus extra to serve

freshly ground black pepper

2 large egg yolks

150ml cooled vegetable stock

salt

low calorie cooking spray

These mini potato mountains are a fab way to add a special touch to dinner. The pungent garlic and rosemary fill the mash with flavour, creating a side dish that complements many a main course!

Place the potatoes in a large saucepan of lightly salted boiling water and cook for 25 minutes or until very tender. Drain well and return to the pan.

Preheat the oven to 200°C/Fan 180°C/Gas 6.

Add the nutmeg, garlic and rosemary to the potatoes, season with black pepper and mash well.

Add the egg yolks, stock and salt to taste and continue to mash until the mixture is smooth. (Do not over-mash or your potatoes will end up with a gluey consistency.)

Using a piping bag with a large star nozzle, pipe the potatoes into swirls (about 4-5cm in diameter) on a baking sheet lined with baking parchment, well spaced apart.

Lightly spray the potato swirls with low calorie cooking spray and bake in the oven for 20-25 minutes or until the edges turn light brown. Remove from the oven, scatter over the extra chopped rosemary and serve.

chocolate, chilli and coffee mousse pots

serves 6

each serving is:

6 Syns on Extra Easy

6 Syns on Green

6 Syns on Original

preparation time: 20 minutes plus chilling/freezing

cooking time: none

125g dark chocolate

4 medium eggs, separated*

4 level tbsp sweetener

½ tsp dried red chilli flakes

2 tsp instant coffee granules dissolved in 1 tbsp water

2 tbsp cognac or brandy

fat free natural fromage frais, to serve

1 level tsp cocoa powder, to dust

orange zest, to decorate

Pregnant women, the elderly and babies are advised not to eat raw or partially cooked eggs.

Rich, fiery and indulgent, this is a really stunning finale to a meal – especially when presented in this cute and quirky way. The sophisticated flavours of chocolate, chilli and coffee with a dash of cognac or brandy make this a dessert to die for!

Break the chocolate into small pieces, place in a large heatproof bowl and melt over a pan of gently simmering water. Remove from the heat and leave to cool slightly at room temperature.

Meanwhile whisk the egg whites in a large bowl until stiff but not too dry.

Whisk the egg yolks, sweetener, chilli flakes, instant coffee mixture and cognac or brandy in a separate bowl and spoon into the melted chocolate, mixing well.

Lightly fold in the egg whites with a metal spoon until well combined. Spoon this mixture into six tea cups or dessert dishes and place in the freezer for 2-3 hours or until just set.

To serve, top each serving with a spoonful of fromage frais, lightly dust with cocoa powder and decorate with orange zest.

poached peaches
with rosewater and pistachios

serves 6

each serving is:

3 Syns on Extra Easy

3 Syns on Green

3 Syns on Original

preparation time: 15 minutes

cooking time: under 45 minutes

6 large, ripe peaches

2 tbsp rosewater

1 cinnamon stick

4 green cardamom pods

8 tbsp sweetener

a few drops of pink food colouring

150g raspberries

1 tbsp very finely chopped pistachio nuts

Juicy peaches topped with speckles of green pistachio and dotted with pink raspberries makes an impressive yet easy-to-prepare pudding.

Peel the peaches by lightly scoring the skin from top to bottom using a small sharp knife. Dip them in a pan of simmering water for 20-30 seconds. Remove the skin carefully under cold running water and discard, then set the peaches aside.

Meanwhile, place the rosewater, cinnamon stick, cardamom pods, sweetener and food colouring in a medium saucepan with 900ml of water and stir to dissolve the sweetener slightly. Place over a high heat and bring the mixture to the boil. Boil for 5 minutes then reduce the heat, leaving the syrup to simmer for 15-20 minutes.

Add the peaches to the pan in a single layer to fit snugly and cook gently for 5-10 minutes (the cooking time will depend on the ripeness of the peaches). Transfer the peaches to a plate with a slotted spoon.

Bring the syrup to the boil and cook for 12-15 minutes or until reduced by about half. Remove from the heat. Pour any juices that have collected from the peaches into the syrup. Strain into a jug and leave to cool to room temperature.

The peaches can be covered with cling film and chilled for several hours, if you like.

When ready to serve, place the peaches in shallow dessert bowls and drizzle with a little of the syrup. Divide the raspberries between the bowls and sprinkle over the chopped pistachios.

You could use apricots or nectarines in place of the peaches for equally tasty results.

Extra Easy Entertaining | *Posh Sunday lunch* | *Desserts*

pink
champagne jellies

serves 6

each serving is:

1 Syn on Extra Easy

1 Syn on Green

1 Syn on Original

preparation time: 15 minutes
plus chilling

cooking time: none

1 sheet of leaf gelatine

2 x 11.5g sachets sugar free
strawberry jelly crystals

100ml pink Champagne or
sparkling rosé wine

6 strawberries,
plus extra to serve

With a total preparation time of 15 minutes, this
is a super pud to pre-prepare. It's light enough
to end a big Sunday lunch and brings a touch of
sparkle thanks to the elegant pink Champagne.

Soak the gelatine in a bowl of cold water for 10 minutes until softened.

Sprinkle the contents of the jelly sachets into a large jug containing
300ml of boiling water and stir to mix well.

Remove the softened gelatine from the bowl, squeeze out the excess
water, add to the jug and stir until dissolved.

Add 300ml of cold water to the jug and mix well. When the jelly has
cooled slightly, add the pink Champagne or wine.

Place a strawberry in the base of six wide Champagne, cocktail or
dessert glasses and pour in the jelly.

Chill in the fridge for at least 6 hours or until just set and serve the
jellies straight from the fridge with the remaining strawberries.

al fresco *treats*

When the sun is shining, nothing beats packing up
our tastiest eats and dining in the great outdoors.
We've rustled up some delicious picnic and barbecue
treats so dust off your deckchairs, put up your
parasol and tuck in!

smoked trout pancake pinwheels

serves 8

each serving is:

Free on Extra Easy

Free on Original

3½ Syns on Green

preparation time: 20 minutes plus chilling

cooking time: under 30 minutes

10 large eggs

8 tbsp finely chopped fresh dill, plus extra sprigs to garnish

salt and freshly ground black pepper

low calorie cooking spray

400g quark

10 spring onions, finely sliced

1 medium cucumber, halved, deseeded and finely diced

1 tbsp finely grated lemon zest and 1 tbsp fresh lemon juice, plus extra lemon wedges to serve

450g thinly sliced smoked trout

These pinwheel pancakes look great and capture the charms of summer with the fresh flavours of smoked trout, dill and cucumber. They're light, refreshing and a tasty way to kick off your al fresco feast!

Beat the eggs in a large measuring jug with the dill and season to taste.

Spray a 22cm frying pan with low calorie cooking spray and, when hot, pour one-sixth of the egg mixture into it. Swirl to coat the base evenly and cook for 2-3 minutes or until the base is lightly set. Remove from the pan with a spatula and place on a clean work surface. Repeat with the remaining egg mixture to make six pancakes in total.

Place the quark in a medium-sized bowl and stir in the spring onions, cucumber and lemon zest and juice. Season with freshly ground black pepper and mix well.

Line the pancakes with smoked trout slices to cover. Spread the quark mixture carefully over the smoked trout with a palette knife.

Roll each pancake up firmly and press to seal. Wrap each roll tightly in cling film and chill for 6-8 hours.

Trim the uneven ends of the rolls if you wish and cut the rolls into thick slices. Serve with lemon wedges and a garnish of fresh dill.

fennel and white bean dip
with summer crudités

serves 8

each serving is:

Free on Extra Easy

Free on Green

3 Syns on Original

preparation time: 15 minutes

cooking time: under 5 minutes

Feeling dippy? You won't fail to impress with this delicately spiced fennel and white bean dip and selection of summer crudités – ideal for a posh picnic.

for the crudités

300g runner beans, trimmed and cut into 4cm diagonal lengths

400g asparagus tips

2 large carrots, peeled and cut into thick batons

8 celery sticks, cut into thick batons

2 red peppers, deseeded and cut into thick batons

for the dip

400g can cannellini beans, drained

400g can butter beans, drained

juice of 1 lemon

1 tsp dried red chilli flakes

1 tbsp fennel seeds

1 tsp smoked paprika

2 garlic cloves, peeled and crushed

300g silken tofu, cut into cubes

a small handful of chopped fresh tarragon, plus extra sprigs to garnish

salt and freshly ground black pepper

Prepare the crudités, then blanch the runner beans and asparagus tips in lightly salted boiling water for 2-3 minutes. Drain well and transfer to a serving platter with the vegetable batons.

Place all the ingredients for the dip in a food processor and blitz until smooth. Season well and transfer to a bowl.

Garnish with sprigs of tarragon and serve at room temperature with the crudités.

Replace the beans in this recipe with canned chickpeas for a 'houmous'-style dip that's Free on Extra Easy and Green.

minted lamb burgers with radish and watercress salad

Bite-sized and bursting with flavour, these minted lamb burgers are packed with meaty magic, making them a barbecue essential. The peppery flavours of the radish and watercress salad complement the lamb perfectly!

Place the lamb in a food processor with the onion, garlic, ginger, red chillies, curry powder, yogurt, lime zest and juice and mint. Season well and blend until well mixed and smooth. Transfer to a bowl, cover and chill for 3-4 hours or overnight if time permits.

Preheat the oven to 180°C/Fan 160°C/Gas 4. Divide the mixture into 16 portions and form each one into a burger shape. Place on a baking sheet lined with baking parchment and lightly spray with low calorie cooking spray. Transfer to the oven and cook for 15-18 minutes or until cooked through.

Meanwhile, make the salad by slicing the radishes very thinly and placing them in a bowl with the sliced onion and the lemon juice. Season well and mix together. Toss in the watercress and divide the salad between eight plates. Top each salad with two burgers and serve immediately.

*You can use **extra lean turkey mince** instead of lamb for this **flavoursome** recipe.*

serves 8

each serving is:

Free on Extra Easy

Free on Original

11½ Syns on Green

❄ (burgers only)

preparation time: 20 minutes plus chilling

cooking time: under 20 minutes

for the burgers

1.2kg lean lamb steaks, all visible fat removed, cut into chunks

1 onion, peeled and finely chopped

2 garlic cloves, peeled and crushed

2cm piece root ginger, peeled and grated

2 red chillies, deseeded and finely chopped

1 tbsp medium curry powder

2 tbsp fat free natural yogurt

finely grated zest and juice of 1 lime

8 tbsp finely chopped fresh mint

salt and freshly ground black pepper

low calorie cooking spray

for the salad

500g red radishes

1 red onion, peeled, halved and very thinly sliced

juice of 1 lemon

75g watercress

griddled pork medallions
with citrus salsa

serves 8

each serving is:

Free on Extra Easy

Free on Original

7½ Syns on Green

preparation time: 20 minutes

cooking time: under 30 minutes

Ideal for a lazy summer afternoon when you want to keep cooking to a minimum, these pork medallions are ready in under 30 minutes. The cool citrusy salsa can be made in advance and makes a perfect partner to your pork.

for the salsa

600g pineapple flesh,
cut into 1.5cm dice

4 large oranges, peeled,
seeded and cut into small dice

1 large red chilli, deseeded
and finely chopped

8 spring onions,
finely diced or sliced

finely grated zest
and juice of 2 limes

a small handful of finely
chopped fresh coriander

salt and freshly ground
black pepper

for the pork

1kg extra lean pork medallions

low calorie cooking spray

1 tbsp dried thyme

Make the salsa by combining all the ingredients in a bowl. Season well, cover and set aside at room temperature for 20-30 minutes.

Spray the medallions with low calorie cooking spray, scatter over the dried thyme and season well.

Heat a large ridged griddle until smoking hot, add the medallions and cook, in batches, for 6-8 minutes on each side or until cooked through.

Serve the medallions with the salsa spooned over.

*This **tangy, zingy salsa** would also make a **great accompaniment** to grilled fish, meat or chicken.*

honey, ginger and mustard beef skewers

Whether they're griddled over hot coals or cooked indoors, these marinated beef skewers are a sure-fire way to warm up your garden get-together.

Make the marinade by placing all the ingredients in a bowl and mixing until smooth.

Place the beef in a large, re-sealable plastic bag and pour in the marinade. Press the air out of the bag and seal tightly. Turn the bag several times to cover the beef in the marinade and leave to marinate at room temperature for 30 minutes or in the fridge for 1 hour, turning occasionally.

Remove the beef from the bag and discard the marinade. Thread the beef and peppers alternately on to 12 metal skewers.

Place the skewers on a grill rack and place under a preheated medium-hot grill. Cook for 5-6 minutes on each side until cooked to your liking.

You can use large chunks of chicken or other lean meat instead of the beef.

serves 8

each serving is:

½ **Syn** on Extra Easy

½ **Syn** on Original

8½ **Syns** on Green

preparation time: 20 minutes plus marinating

cooking time: under 15 minutes

for the marinade

1 tsp ground star anise

7.5cm piece root ginger, peeled and finely grated

1 level tbsp runny honey

4 tbsp light soy sauce

2 tsp mustard powder

100g fat free natural yogurt

finely grated zest and juice of 1 lime

for the skewers

1kg lean beef steaks, all visible fat removed, cut into 2.5cm pieces

3 yellow peppers, deseeded and cut into 2.5cm pieces

2 red peppers, deseeded and cut into 2.5cm pieces

tuna with roasted
red pepper couscous

serves 8

each serving is:

Free on Extra Easy

11 Syns on Original

12 Syns on Green

preparation time: 25 minutes

cooking time: under 30 minutes

Fresh flavours and bright colours make this griddled tuna and couscous salad a substantial dish that'll be a huge hit with your guests. Sweet roasted red peppers are a super addition to grilled fish and meat – pepper perfection!

for the couscous

500g couscous

500g green beans, trimmed and halved

400g bottled roasted red peppers in brine/vinegar, drained and roughly chopped

4 tbsp capers, rinsed

finely grated zest and juice of 1 large lemon

2 garlic cloves, peeled and crushed

4 tbsp each of finely chopped fresh mint and parsley

8 spring onions, finely chopped or sliced

salt and freshly ground black pepper

for the tuna

8 tuna steaks (approx 175g each)

low calorie cooking spray

Place the couscous in a wide heatproof bowl and just cover with boiling hot water. Cover with cling film and allow to stand for around 15 minutes or until all the liquid is absorbed.

Meanwhile cook the green beans in a large saucepan of lightly salted boiling water for 5 minutes. Drain the beans and add to the couscous with all the remaining ingredients. Season well and set aside.

Season the tuna steaks and spray with low calorie cooking spray. Heat a large ridged griddle until smoking, add the steaks and cook in batches for 2 minutes on each side or until cooked to your liking (or cook them on a prepared barbecue).

Divide the couscous between eight plates and top each with a tuna steak.

mixed seafood grill
with herb mayonnaise

serves 8

each serving is:

½ **Syn** on Extra Easy

½ **Syn** on Original

34 Syns on Green

preparation time: 30 minutes

cooking time: under 30 minutes

Summon memories of the seaside by making this seafood platter of salmon, cod, prawns, mussels and squid your catch of the day! Save an ocean of Syns by serving your seafood sharer with a cool and creamy homemade herb mayonnaise dip.

for the herb mayonnaise

2 garlic cloves, peeled and crushed

1 red chilli, deseeded (optional) and finely chopped

6 tbsp each of finely chopped mint, parsley and tarragon

250g silken tofu, roughly chopped

250g quark

4 level tbsp extra-light mayonnaise

salt and freshly ground black pepper

for the seafood grill

10 thick skinless salmon fillets

10 thick skinless halibut or cod fillets

low calorie cooking spray

24 large raw tiger prawns

24 fresh mussels

600g squid, cleaned and cut into 3cm pieces

6 tbsp finely chopped fresh parsley

finely grated zest and juice of 2 lemons

Make the herb mayonnaise by placing all the ingredients in a food processor and blending until smooth. Season well and chill until ready to serve.

Cut the fish fillets into large bite-sized pieces and place on a grill rack. Season well, spray with low calorie cooking spray and place under a medium-hot grill for 6-8 minutes until cooked through. Remove from the heat, cover and keep warm.

Place the prawns and mussels on a baking tray in a single layer and cook under a medium-hot grill for 6-8 minutes or until the prawns have turned pink and the mussels have opened (discard any that remain closed). Remove from the heat and keep warm.

Lightly score the cut side of the squid in a criss-cross pattern with a sharp knife and pat dry with kitchen paper. Lightly spray with low calorie cooking spray, season and cook on a smoking hot griddle for 1-2 minutes. Remove from the heat and arrange on a wide serving platter with the rest of the grilled fish and seafood.

Scatter over the chopped parsley and lemon zest and juice and serve the mixed seafood grill with the herb mayonnaise. (Offer finger bowls of warm water with lemon slices in so you can all clean your hands as you eat.)

creamy chicken, bacon and rigatoni salad

Traditional Italian cooking is bursting with robust flavours and this chicken, bacon and pasta salad is no exception. It's perfect for those lazy afternoons when you fancy a hearty salad in the sunshine without any hassle – and it's ideal for picnic baskets and packed lunches, too.

Preheat the oven to 200°C/Fan 180°C/Gas 6. Cook the pasta according to the packet instructions. Drain, rinse under cold running water, drain again and set aside.

Meanwhile place the tomatoes, cut side up, on a baking sheet lined with baking parchment. Scatter over the garlic, spray with low calorie cooking spray and roast in the oven for 15 minutes.

Grill the bacon rashers under a medium-hot grill for around 5 minutes on each side or until crisp and lightly golden. Break into bite-sized pieces and set aside on kitchen paper.

Make the dressing by blending all the ingredients in a food processor until smooth. Season to taste and set aside.

Arrange the pasta, lettuce, cucumber and roasted tomatoes on a wide salad platter and scatter over the bacon and chicken. Drizzle over the dressing, scatter over the chives, toss to mix well and serve.

serves 8

each serving is:

½ **Syn** on Extra Easy

13½ **Syns** on Original

18½ **Syns** on Green

preparation time: 30 minutes

cooking time: under 20 minutes

for the salad

600g rigatoni pasta

600g midi vine tomatoes, halved

3 garlic cloves, peeled and finely chopped

low calorie cooking spray

550g lean dry-smoked bacon rashers, all visible fat removed

6 baby gem lettuces, leaves separated

1 large cucumber, halved lengthways, deseeded and sliced

8 cooked, skinless and boneless chicken breasts, roughly chopped

a large handful of finely chopped fresh chives

for the dressing

1 tsp English mustard powder mixed with 2 tbsp water

400g low fat natural cottage cheese

200g quark

6 level tbsp extra-light mayonnaise

½ tsp sweetener

finely grated zest and juice of 1 lemon

salt and freshly ground black pepper

halloumi and vegetable skewers

serves 8

each serving is:

8 Syns on Extra Easy

8 Syns on Green

8 Syns on Original

preparation time: 20 minutes

cooking time: under 10 minutes

A feast for your eyes as well as your stomach, these colourful halloumi and vegetable skewers are packed with Mediterranean sunshine – and will leave everyone with a smile!

for the marinade

200ml fat free French dressing

finely grated zest and juice of 1 lemon

2 tsp ground cumin

2 red chillies, deseeded and finely diced

4 garlic cloves, peeled and finely chopped

salt and freshly ground black pepper

lime wedges, to serve

for the skewers

2 courgettes, cut into bite-sized pieces

2 red peppers, deseeded and cut into bite-sized pieces

2 yellow peppers, deseeded and cut into bite-sized pieces

2 medium red onions, peeled and cut into wedges

400g firm halloumi cheese, cut into small bite-sized pieces

low calorie cooking spray

Make the marinade by mixing all the ingredients in a bowl. Season to taste and set aside.

Thread eight medium-sized metal skewers with the courgettes, peppers, onions and halloumi, and place on a grill rack in a single layer. Brush most of the marinade over the cheese and vegetable skewers.

Lightly spray the skewers with low calorie cooking spray and place the grill rack under a preheated medium-hot grill (you could also cook them on the barbecue).

Cook the skewers for around 5 minutes on each side, brushing with the remaining marinade until lightly browned at the edges.

Remove from the grill and serve with lime wedges to squeeze over.

tofu and chickpea burgers

Every barbecue needs a veggie option and these tofu and chickpea burgers are the perfect choice. Made from scratch in a flash and full of Middle Eastern flavours, they're guaranteed to be a talking point.

Cook the potatoes in a large saucepan of lightly salted boiling water for around 15 minutes, until tender. Drain thoroughly, transfer to a mixing bowl, mash well and leave to cool.

Place the chickpeas in a blender or food processor with the egg yolks, garlic, spices, chopped coriander and spring onions and blend until fairly smooth. Season, add to the cooled potato mixture and stir in the tofu. Mash and mix well.

Divide the mixture into eight portions and form into burgers. Place on a baking sheet lined with baking parchment, cover with cling film and chill in the fridge for a minimum of 6 hours or overnight if time permits.

When ready to cook, spray the burgers with low calorie cooking spray. Cook in a preheated oven for around 15 minutes at 180°C/Fan 160°C/Gas 4 until lightly golden. Scatter with chopped coriander.

These are great served in toasted wholemeal rolls (6 Syns per 60g roll), with lettuce leaves, slices of tomato and onion and topped with a spoon of passata.

makes 8

each burger is:

Free on Extra Easy

Free on Green

4½ Syns on Original

preparation time: 25 minutes plus chilling

cooking time: under 30 minutes

600g Desirée potatoes, peeled and roughly chopped

410g can chickpeas, drained

2 egg yolks

2 garlic cloves, peeled and crushed

1 tsp crushed coriander seeds

1 tbsp medium curry powder

2 tsp black onion seeds (nigella seeds)

a large handful of finely chopped fresh coriander, plus extra to serve

6 spring onions, finely chopped

salt and freshly ground black pepper

200g tofu (plain or naturally smoked), finely chopped or diced

low calorie cooking spray

carrot and
celeriac rémoulade

serves 8

each serving is:

Free on Extra Easy

Free on Green

Free on Original

preparation time: 25 minutes

cooking time: none

---

1 large celeriac

3 large carrots, peeled

200g fat free natural fromage frais

1 level tbsp Dijon mustard

fresh lemon juice

salt and freshly ground
black pepper

4 tbsp small capers, rinsed

75g bottled roasted red peppers
in brine/vinegar, drained and finely
chopped

This sweet carrot and celeriac dish is a Free version of the classic French salad. This full-of-flavour side dish is ready in just minutes and brings lots of Superfree goodness into your al fresco feast.

Peel the celeriac and cut into wedges. Use a food processor fitted with a grating disc to grate the celeriac and carrots into long, elegant strands. Alternatively, you could use a mandolin or a vegetable peeler with a shredder attachment.

Put the fromage frais, mustard and a squeeze of lemon juice in a large mixing bowl and beat until well combined. Season to taste and stir in the capers and roasted red peppers.

Add the grated celeriac and carrots to the bowl and stir to coat well.

Arrange the celeriac mixture on a serving dish and grind a little black pepper over the top before serving at room temperature.

griddled fennel
and tomato salad

serves 8

each serving is:

Free on Extra Easy

Free on Green

Free on Original

preparation time: 15 minutes

cooking time: under 30 minutes

---

2 large fennel bulbs, trimmed, halved, cored and cut lengthwise into 8 wedges

1 large onion, peeled and cut into 1cm thick rings

low calorie cooking spray

8 large red tomatoes, quartered

salt and freshly ground black pepper

4 tbsp Champagne vinegar or white wine vinegar

juice of 1 lemon

2 garlic cloves, peeled and crushed

1 level tsp Dijon mustard

100ml fat free French dressing

a small handful of fresh basil leaves

Superfree and super-tasty, this griddled summer salad is a great accompaniment to barbecued meat and fish. Delicious served warm, the blackened edges of the vegetables add a smoky flavour to this stunning side dish!

Spray the fennel and onion with low calorie cooking spray and cook on a smoking hot ridged griddle, in batches, for 4-5 minutes until lightly charred at the edges.

Transfer to a foil-lined baking tray and add the tomatoes. Season well.

Mix the vinegar, lemon juice, garlic, mustard and French dressing in a small bowl. Spoon this over the vegetables, cover with foil to form a parcel and place under a preheated medium-hot grill for 5-7 minutes.

Remove from the grill and carefully remove the foil. Transfer to a serving dish and scatter over the basil leaves before serving warm or at room temperature.

grilled summer vegetable and potato salad

serves 8

each serving is:

Free on Extra Easy

Free on Green

2 Syns on Original

preparation time: 20 minutes

cooking time: under 30 minutes

for the salad

400g new potatoes,
scrubbed and thickly sliced

3 medium aubergines,
cut into 1cm thick slices

3 large courgettes,
cut into 1cm thick slices

low calorie cooking spray

salt and freshly ground
black pepper

a large handful of fresh mint

2 tsp black onion seeds
(nigella seeds)

200g pomegranate seeds

smoked paprika, to sprinkle

for the dressing

1 red chilli, deseeded
and finely diced

2 garlic cloves, peeled and crushed

200g fat free natural fromage frais

juice of 1 orange

½ tsp ground cinnamon

1 tsp ground cumin

25g each of fresh coriander
and mint, finely chopped

Use summer's bounty of fresh courgettes, aubergines and basil in this crowd-pleasing potato salad. The sprinkle of sweet pomegranate seeds add a touch of colour and a delicious hint of the Middle East.

Boil the potatoes in a saucepan of lightly salted boiling water for about 10-12 minutes or until just tender. Drain thoroughly.

Preheat the grill to high. Put the aubergine and courgette slices on a baking sheet, spray lightly with low calorie cooking spray and season well.

Grill for about 15 minutes, turning halfway through and spraying with low calorie cooking spray, until browned and softened. Alternatively, you can cook them on a hot griddle, in batches.

Arrange the courgette, aubergine and potato slices on a serving platter.

Make the dressing by blending all the ingredients until fairly smooth. Season well.

Drizzle the dressing over the vegetables, scatter over the mint, black onion seeds and pomegranate seeds and sprinkle with paprika just before serving.

*This **colourful** and **tasty salad** can be made **ahead of time** and served at room temperature.*

summer rice salad
with mixed beans

This all-in-one side dish can double up as a veggie main course, perfect for relaxed summer dining. It's ready in under 30 minutes and any leftovers can be loaded into your lunchbox for the next day.

serves 8

each serving is:

Free on Extra Easy

Free on Green

9½ Syns on Original

❄ Ⓥ

preparation time: 20 minutes

cooking time: under 20 minutes

Put the onion, garlic and 100ml of stock into a heavy-based saucepan. Cover with a tight-fitting lid and soften the onion over a low heat.

Increase the heat to high, add the ginger, red pepper, cumin seeds and chilli flakes and cook, stirring, for 3-4 minutes. Stir in the rice.

Pour in the remaining stock, bring to a simmer, cover and cook over a low heat for 10 minutes. Remove from the heat and leave for 10 minutes with the lid on.

Fork through the beans, lime zest and chopped coriander. Season well and serve warm or at room temperature.

1 large red onion, peeled and finely chopped

2 garlic cloves, peeled and finely chopped

750ml hot vegetable stock

1 tsp ground ginger

1 red pepper, deseeded and cut into 1cm cubes

3 tsp cumin seeds

½ tsp dried red chilli flakes

300g basmati rice or long-grain rice

400g can red kidney beans, drained and rinsed

400g can black-eyed beans, drained and rinsed

finely grated zest of 1 lime

a small handful of fresh coriander, leaves chopped

salt and freshly ground black pepper

mixed melon ice pops

makes 8

each ice pop is:

1½ Syns on Extra Easy

1½ Syns on Green

1½ Syns on Original

preparation time: 10 minutes plus freezing

cooking time: none

300g fresh watermelon flesh, roughly chopped

4 tbsp sweetener

finely grated zest and juice of 1 lime

1 cantaloupe melon, halved and seeded

Cool off with these refreshing mixed melon ice lollies for only 1½ Syns each! They're the perfect make-ahead summer sweet treat and will be loved by children and adults alike!

Place the watermelon in a food processor with half of the sweetener and half of the lime zest and juice. Blend until smooth then transfer to a jug.

Scoop the cantaloupe flesh into a food processor with the remaining sweetener, lime zest and juice and blend until smooth. Transfer to a jug and chill in the fridge.

Half-fill eight 100ml ice-pop moulds with the watermelon mixture. Insert an ice cream stick into each mould and freeze for 3-4 hours or until just firm.

Pour the chilled cantaloupe melon mixture into the moulds and return to the freezer for 4-5 hours or until firm.

To serve, dip the moulds into warm water for a few seconds to remove the ice pops.

seared nectarines with sweet spiced yogurt

Round off an idyllic al fresco dinner by grilling or barbecuing juicy nectarines and serving with sweet-spiced yogurt. This delicious summer dessert is just 2½ Syns per serving and tastes simply divine.

First make the spiced yogurt. Mix all the ingredients in a bowl, cover and freeze for at least 30 minutes before serving.

Place the nectarines, cut side up, on a clean work surface. Mix the sweetener and cinnamon together and sprinkle over the nectarines.

When ready to cook, heat a barbecue or griddle until hot and cook the nectarines for 2-3 minutes on each side or until lightly charred at the edges.

Divide the fruit between eight dessert plates and serve with the chilled sweet-spiced yogurt, decorated with mint sprigs.

Other firm stone fruits like **peaches** *or* **apricots** *taste equally* **delicious** *cooked over coals.*

serves 8

each serving is:

2½ **Syns** on Extra Easy

2½ **Syns** on Green

2½ **Syns** on Original

preparation time: 10 minutes plus 30 minutes' freezing

cooking time: under 20 minutes

for the yogurt

¼ tsp crushed cardamom seeds

¼ tsp crushed star anise

1 tsp ground cinnamon

¼ tsp ground ginger

700g fat free natural yogurt

1 tsp vanilla essence

2 tbsp sweetener

for the nectarines

12 firm, ripe nectarines, halved and stones removed

2 tbsp sweetener

2 tsp ground cinnamon

mint sprigs, to decorate

buffet
party

These bite-sized nibbles look delicious on platters and
they're easy to eat while standing, mingling and juggling drinks!
Create a feast fit for a king (all you can eat buffet-style!)
and stay on track for a wonderful weight loss with these
fab Food Optimising-friendly ideas.

bacon and
beef sliders

makes 20 sliders

each slider is:

Free on Extra Easy

Free on Original

3½ Syns on Green

preparation time: 20 minutes

cooking time: under 15 minutes

---

low calorie cooking spray

2 garlic cloves, peeled and crushed

1 onion, very finely chopped

4 lean bacon rashers, all visible fat removed, very finely chopped

1kg extra-lean minced beef

a good splash of Worcestershire sauce

a dash of Tabasco sauce

a small handful of chopped fresh chives

a small handful of finely chopped fresh flat-leaf parsley

salt and freshly ground black pepper

romaine or little gem lettuce leaves, 10 halved cherry tomatoes and 20 small gherkins, to serve

A healthy spin on the mini burger, these trendy bite-size snacks are all the rage at social events. Loaded with all the goodies and packed with flavour, they look great on the buffet table.

Spray a frying pan with low calorie cooking spray and cook the garlic, onion and bacon over a medium-low heat for around 5 minutes until softened.

Cool slightly, then transfer to a large bowl with the minced beef, Worcestershire sauce and Tabasco sauce. Add the chopped herbs, season to taste and mix well. Divide into 20 portions and shape into small burgers or 'sliders'.

Cook the sliders under a preheated medium-hot grill for 8-10 minutes or until cooked to your liking.

Line a serving platter with lettuce leaves and put a slider on each one. Using a cocktail stick, skewer half a cherry tomato and a gherkin on to each slider and serve.

herbed
chicken skewers

serves 10

each serving is:

Free on Extra Easy

Free on Original

9½ Syns on Green

preparation time: 10 minutes
plus overnight marinating

cooking time: 10 minutes

---

12 skinless chicken breast fillets,
cut into bite-sized pieces

finely grated zest
and juice of 1 lime

250g fat free natural yogurt

1cm piece root ginger,
peeled and finely grated

3 garlic cloves, peeled and crushed

1 red chilli, deseeded and chopped

a large handful of finely chopped
fresh coriander and mint

2 tbsp medium curry powder

3 tbsp light soy sauce

lime wedges, to serve

Pep up plain chicken with a marinade of
mouth-watering herbs and spices. Whack them
under the grill or throw them on the barbie –
these succulent skewers will go down a treat
with family and friends either way.

Put the chicken in a large bowl. Using a blender or food processor,
blend the remaining ingredients until fairly smooth, adding a little
water if necessary.

Pour the marinade over the chicken and toss to mix well. Cover and
leave in the fridge overnight.

When ready to cook, preheat the grill until hot. Thread the chicken
on to 20 metal skewers (or pre-soaked bamboo skewers) and grill for
around 10 minutes, turning once or twice, until the chicken is cooked
through.

Serve immediately with lime wedges for squeezing over.

Marinate the chicken overnight
to make it really tender and tasty.

honey and
mustard glazed ham

serves 10

each serving is:

1½ Syns on Extra Easy

1½ Syns on Original

34½ Syns on Green

preparation time: 30 minutes

cooking time: 4 hours

for the ham

5kg very lean good quality ham joint

10 black peppercorns

5 fresh bay leaves

2 celery sticks

1 onion, peeled and chopped

3 carrots, peeled
and roughly chopped

for the glaze

3 level tbsp runny honey

5 level tbsp English mustard

2 tbsp sweetener

finely grated zest of 1 orange

a handful of cloves

Take your guests to hog heaven with a slice of gorgeous glazed ham! Traditional, tender and slightly spicy in flavour, it makes a feast fit for any table and, because the ham is cooked slowly, you'll have plenty of time to prepare the rest of the buffet!

Place the ham into a large pot and add the peppercorns, bay leaves and vegetables. Pour over enough water to cover the meat and vegetables, and cover the pan with a tight-fitting lid. Bring to the boil then immediately turn down the heat.

Simmer the ham gently for 3½ hours, topping up with water as necessary. When the ham is cooked, the meat will be firm. Remove the pot from the heat and leave the ham to cool in the cooking broth.

Preheat the oven to 180°C/Fan 160°C/Gas 4. Make the glaze by mixing the honey, mustard, sweetener and orange zest until you have a loose paste, adding a little water if necessary.

Transfer the ham joint to a clean work surface and discard the cooking liquid and vegetables. Remove any skin and fat from the ham, score the flesh evenly all over, and stud each diamond shape with a clove.

Brush half of the glaze evenly over the outside of the ham and place on a baking tray on the middle shelf of the oven.

Roast for 10 minutes then brush the rest of the glaze on top. Cook for 20 minutes or until sticky, golden brown and slightly set. Cut into thin slices and serve with English mustard (½ Syn per level teaspoon).

*For a **tastier**, even more **tender result**, soak the ham for 6-8 hours in cold water (changed regularly) to absorb excess salt from the meat.*

sticky hoisin cocktail sausages

Plain cocktail sausages get a sizzling makeover with this speedy and simple, sweet and savoury recipe. Fused with Asian flavours, these porky little delights will leave everyone wanting more!

makes 20

each sausage is:

1½ Syns on Extra Easy

1½ Syns on Original

2 Syns on Green

preparation time: 10 minutes

cooking time: under 30 minutes

20 pork cocktail sausages

2 level tbsp hoisin sauce

4 tbsp tomato purée

4 tbsp dark soy sauce

¼ tsp sweetener

¼ tsp dried red chilli flakes

Preheat the oven to 180°C/Fan 160°C/Gas 4. Place the sausages in a large mixing bowl.

Mix together the hoisin sauce, tomato purée, soy sauce, sweetener and chilli flakes. Pour over the sausages and toss to mix well.

Place the sausages in a single layer in a roasting tin lined with baking parchment. Roast in the oven for 25-30 minutes or until sticky and cooked through.

Serve warm or at room temperature.

crustless cheddar, onion and courgette quiche

serves 10

each serving is:

3 Syns on Extra Easy

3 Syns on Green

3 Syns on Original

preparation time: 30 minutes

cooking time: about 1½ hours

---

low calorie cooking spray

4 onions, peeled,
halved and thinly sliced

3 large courgettes, thinly sliced

300g bottled roasted red peppers
in brine/vinegar, drained and finely
chopped

12 large eggs

2 garlic cloves, peeled and crushed

4 tbsp tomato purée

2 tsp dried mixed herbs

200g reduced fat Cheddar
cheese, grated

salt and freshly ground
black pepper

Who says making quiche has to be complicated? This versatile veggie version with a twist is perfect for informal entertaining or family dinners. There's no need to fiddle about with pastry and you can enjoy it when it's hot – and when it's not!

Preheat the oven to 180°C/Fan 160°C/Gas 4.

Spray a large frying pan with low calorie cooking spray and sauté the onions over a medium-low heat for around 15 minutes until lightly browned. Transfer to a wide bowl and set aside.

Wipe the frying pan with kitchen paper and re-spray with low calorie cooking spray. Place over a medium heat, add the courgette and stir-fry for around 10 minutes or until lightly browned. Remove from the heat and add to the onions along with the roasted red peppers.

Beat the eggs with the garlic, tomato purée, dried herbs and three-quarters of the cheese. Season well.

Lightly spray a round, ceramic deep pie dish (about 30cm across) with low calorie cooking spray.

Put the onions, courgettes and red peppers in the prepared dish and pour over the egg mixture. Bake in the oven for for 40-45 minutes until almost set.

Sprinkle over the remaining cheese and return to the oven for another 15 minutes or until lightly browned on top and just set.

Remove from the oven and serve warm or at room temperature, cut into wedges.

Replace the Cheddar cheese with creamy blue cheese for a different flavour.

hot-smoked salmon and new potato salad platter

If you love salmon you'll fall for this sophisticated salad hook, line and sinker! Subtle flavours of smoked fish, fresh watercress and quail eggs combine with the humble potato to create an elegant addition to any buffet table.

Make the dressing by whisking all the ingredients together in a bowl. Season to taste and set aside.

Cook the potatoes in a large saucepan of lightly salted boiling water for 15-20 minutes or until just tender. Drain, cool slightly, then halve.

While the potatoes are cooking, blanch the green beans in plenty of boiling water for 4-5 minutes until cooked but still with a slight crunch. Drain, refresh in iced water, then drain again.

Cook the quail eggs in a saucepan of boiling water for 3-4 minutes. Drain, cool under cold running water, then peel.

Arrange the watercress on a large platter and top with the potatoes, green beans, salmon, spring onions, quail eggs and tomatoes. Scatter over the mustard and cress and drizzle over the dressing. Toss gently to mix well before serving.

Quail eggs are available in most supermarkets but you can use six hen eggs, halved and quartered, if you prefer.

serves 10

each serving is:

Free on Extra Easy

2 Syns on Original

4½ Syns on Green

preparation time: 40 minutes

cooking time: under 30 minutes

for the dressing

10 tbsp fat free salad dressing

1 level tbsp wholegrain mustard

2 tbsp finely chopped dill

juice of 1 orange

salt and freshly ground black pepper

for the salad

600g small new potatoes

200g green beans, trimmed

12 quail eggs

200g watercress

600g hot-smoked salmon, skinned and flaked into large chunks

8 spring onions, thinly sliced

400g red cherry tomatoes, halved

1 punnet mustard and cress

asian
prawn noodle salad

serves 10

each serving is:

½ **Syn** on Extra Easy

2½ **Syns** on Green

9½ **Syns** on Original

preparation time: 30 minutes

cooking time: 10 minutes

500g thin cellophane or
bean thread noodles

low calorie cooking spray

3 garlic cloves, peeled
and finely chopped

2cm piece root ginger,
peeled and grated

1 tsp Chinese five-spice seasoning

500g raw tiger prawns, peeled
(tails can be left on if preferred)

1 red pepper, deseeded
and cut into thin strips

¼ tsp sweetener

8 spring onions, finely shredded

1 cucumber, deseeded
and cut into thin matchsticks

2 large carrots, peeled and
cut into thin matchsticks

juice of 4 limes

4 level tbsp sweet chilli sauce

4 tbsp light soy sauce

1 tbsp nam pla (Thai fish sauce)

2 red chillies, deseeded
and thinly sliced

a large handful each of roughly
chopped coriander and mint

salt and freshly ground
black pepper

spring onion slivers and
lime slices, to garnish

Turn plain prawns into something special with
this fantastic stir-fry featuring oodles of noodles.
Low in fat and high in flavour, this Asian-
inspired salad will fill you up and has a citrusy
zing that's perfect for awakening tired senses!

Soak the noodles in a wide bowl of hot water until soft (about
5-6 minutes), then drain, rinse under cold running water, drain
again and return to the bowl.

Spray a large wok or frying pan with low calorie cooking spray and
place over a medium heat. Add the garlic, ginger, five-spice seasoning,
prawns, red pepper and sweetener and stir-fry for 4-5 minutes or until
the prawns turn pink and are cooked through.

Remove from the heat and stir in the drained noodles.

Add the spring onions, cucumber, carrots, lime juice, sweet chilli
sauce, soy sauce, nam pla, red chillies and chopped herbs. Toss to
mix well and check the seasoning.

Serve the salad at room temperature, garnished with spring onion
slivers and the lime slices to squeeze over.

*This is a **very versatile** dish so you
can swap the prawns for **another kind**
of **seafood**, **fish** or **meat** if you prefer.*

beetroot and chickpea couscous salad

Give couscous a new lease of life and bring a rainbow of colour to your table with this satisfying salad, which will help you on your way to five a day!

serves 10

each serving is:

Free on Extra Easy

Free on Green

11½ Syns on Original

preparation time: 20 minutes

cooking time: under 20 minutes

600g dried couscous

1 tsp each of ground ginger, ground cumin and ground cinnamon

salt and freshly ground black pepper

low calorie cooking spray

1 large onion, peeled and roughly chopped

2 red peppers and 2 yellow peppers, deseeded and cut into 1.5cm pieces

100ml boiling hot vegetable stock

400g cooked beetroot, cut into 1.5cm cubes

400g can chickpeas, drained

a large handful of chopped fresh dill

8 tbsp fat free salad dressing

Place the couscous in a wide heatproof bowl with the ground spices, season well and pour over boiling hot water to just cover the grains. Stir to mix well, cover tightly and allow to absorb the water for 12-15 minutes.

Meanwhile, spray a large frying pan with low calorie cooking spray and place over a medium heat. Add the onion and peppers and stir-fry for 8-10 minutes.

Turn the heat to high and add the boiling hot stock. Stir and cook for 2-3 minutes or until the vegetables are softened but still retain a bite.

Fluff up the couscous grains with a fork. Stir in the beetroot, chickpeas, onion mixture and chopped dill. Drizzle over the dressing and toss to mix well. Serve warm or at room temperature.

This is comfort food at its best!
Once you've mastered the basic recipe,
experiment with different vegetables
and spices for new taste sensations.

quinoa, mango
and mint salad

A wonderful way to enjoy quinoa, this crunchy dish is filling, fast and healthy, so it's great when you have lots of hungry mouths to feed! A little bit of summer on a plate, it really does taste as good as it looks.

serves 10

each serving is:

Free on Extra Easy

Free on Green

9 Syns on Original

preparation time: 15 minutes

cooking time: 15 minutes

Cook the quinoa according to the packet instructions, drain well and set aside.

Meanwhile, make the dressing by mixing all the ingredients in a bowl.

Place the quinoa on a wide serving platter with the mango, spinach, tomatoes, pomegranate seeds and mint.

Pour over the dressing, season to taste and toss to mix well.

Serve at room temperature.

for the salad

500g quinoa

600g mango flesh, cut into bite-sized cubes

100g baby spinach leaves

8 plum tomatoes, roughly chopped

200g pomegranate seeds

a large handful of roughly torn mint

salt and freshly ground black pepper

for the dressing

200ml fat free French dressing

juice of 2 limes

2cm piece root ginger, peeled and finely grated

2 red chillies, deseeded and finely chopped

You can use COUSCOUS or bulgur wheat instead of quinoa if you prefer.

trio of delicious dips

minted pea houmous

serves 10

each serving is:

Free on Extra Easy

Free on Green

3½ Syns on Original

preparation time: 15 minutes

cooking time: under 5 minutes

300g frozen peas

2 x 400g cans chickpeas, drained

2 garlic cloves, peeled and crushed

200g fat free natural or
fat free Greek natural yogurt

1 tsp ground cumin

finely grated zest and
juice of 2 lemons

salt and freshly ground
black pepper

25g mint leaves, roughly chopped,
plus extra sprigs to garnish

Blanch the peas in a pan of lightly salted boiling water for 2 minutes. Drain, refresh under cold running water and drain again.

Place the remaining ingredients, except the mint, in a food processor with the drained peas and blend to a fairly smooth mix, scraping down the sides of the processor if you need to.

Season the houmous generously, then add the mint and pulse until roughly chopped. Transfer to a serving bowl and garnish with mint sprigs.

tomato and sweet pepper

serves 10

each serving is:

Free on Extra Easy

Free on Green

Free on Original

preparation time: 15 minutes

cooking time: none

---

2 x 375g jars mild sweet peppadew peppers in brine/vinegar, drained

4 ripe tomatoes, peeled, deseeded and chopped

200g low fat natural cottage cheese

2 tbsp tomato purée

a small handful of freshly chopped basil, plus extra leaves to garnish

salt and freshly ground
black pepper

Place all the ingredients in a blender or food processor and blend until fairly smooth. Season to taste, transfer to a serving bowl and garnish with basil leaves.

creamy smoked aubergine

serves 10

each serving is:

Free on Extra Easy

Free on Green

Free on Original

preparation time: 15 minutes

cooking time: 30 minutes

---

4 large aubergines

200g fat free natural fromage frais

juice of ½ lemon

2 garlic cloves, peeled and crushed

1 red chilli, deseeded
and finely chopped

2 tsp smoked paprika,
plus extra to serve

a pinch of ground cinnamon

a small handful of freshly
chopped coriander

salt and freshly ground
black pepper

Preheat the oven to 240°C/ Fan 220°C/Gas 9. Place the aubergines in the oven for 30 minutes or until the skin is charred. Slice them open and scoop the flesh into a food processor (discard the skin) with the fromage frais, lemon juice, garlic, red chilli, smoked paprika, ground cinnamon and chopped coriander, and season to taste. Blend until fairly smooth then transfer to a serving bowl and sprinkle with the extra paprika.

berry fruit
jelly trifle

Trifle is one of Britain's greatest contributions to dessert cuisine, and no party is complete without one. This two-layered treat combines fresh fruit and light berry jelly with smooth, creamy custard in an utterly delicious offering.

Make the jelly according to the packet instructions and allow to cool.

Place the fruit in the base of a 2-litre glass bowl and pour over the cooled jelly mixture. Chill for 4-5 hours or until just set.

When the jelly is set, pour the custard over the top.

Whisk the fromage frais with the vanilla essence and sweetener and, using a spoon, swirl it over the custard.

Decorate the trifle with the orange zest and dust lightly with the cocoa powder.

serves 10

each serving is:

4 Syns on Extra Easy

4 Syns on Green

4 Syns on Original

preparation time: 15 minutes plus cooling and chilling

cooking time: none

---

4 x 11.5g sachets sugar free raspberry jelly crystals

800g mixed fresh berries (blackberries, blueberries, raspberries and strawberries), plus extra to garnish

850g low fat custard

600g fat free natural fromage frais

1 tsp vanilla essence

2 tbsp sweetener

finely grated orange zest and 1 level tsp cocoa powder, to decorate

tropical fruit salad
with ginger, mint and lime sugar

serves 10

each serving is:

½ **Syn** on Extra Easy

½ **Syn** on Green

½ **Syn** on Original

preparation time: 30 minutes

cooking time: none

---

2 ripe pineapples

6 mangoes

½ watermelon

6 kiwi fruits

200g red seedless grapes

juice of 2 limes

for the sugar

a small handful of mint, finely chopped

1 tsp ground ginger

finely grated zest of 2 limes

2 level tbsp caster sugar

2 tsp sweetener

Paradise on a plate, this tutti frutti salad promises to take your tastebuds to an exotic faraway place! Refreshing, zingy and packed with tantalising flavours, it makes a mouth-watering end to any meal.

Using a sharp knife, trim and peel off the skin of the pineapples. Slice each pineapple in half lengthways and cut out the hard core that runs down its centre. Cut the flesh into bite-sized chunks and place them in a bowl.

Cut the flesh of the mangoes off the stone and scoop out the flesh from the skin with a spoon. Place into the bowl with the pineapple.

Cut the rind off the watermelon, seed the flesh and cut into bite-sized pieces. Place with the mango mixture in the bowl.

Peel the kiwi fruit, cut the flesh into bite-sized pieces and add to the bowl with the pineapple and mango. Add the grapes and drizzle the lime juice over the fruit.

For the sugar: mix the mint leaves with the ground ginger, lime zest, sugar and sweetener and pound until well mixed. Sprinkle over the salad and serve.

This dessert is best when using soft ripe fruit. Give your fruit a squeeze to make sure it meets the 'ripe' test.

feeding
a crowd

*Expecting a large number of guests? Feed your family
and friends without getting in a flap with our crowd-pleasing
recipes for soups, salads, stir-fries, curries, bakes, tarts
– and so much more!*

saigon chicken
noodle soup

serves 10

each serving is:

Free on Extra Easy

6½ Syns on Green

9 Syns on Original

preparation time: 20 minutes

cooking time: 40 minutes

3.5 litres chicken stock

2 star anise

2 cinnamon sticks

8 large, skinless and
boneless chicken breasts

2.5cm piece root ginger,
peeled and grated

6 garlic cloves, peeled
and thinly sliced

500g dried thin egg
or wheat noodles

200g baby sweetcorn,
diagonally cut into thin slices

200g shiitake mushrooms,
thinly sliced

10 spring onions, finely shredded

1 carrot, peeled and
cut into matchsticks

200g mangetout, halved lengthways

6 tbsp light soy sauce

a small handful of mint leaves

2 red chillies, deseeded
and thinly sliced lengthways

This hearty chicken and vegetable Vietnamese soup is delicately flavoured with star anise and cinnamon. If your friends are big fans of Oriental flavours then this soup is a must for your first course.

Pour the stock into a large saucepan and add the star anise, cinnamon sticks, chicken, ginger and garlic.

Bring to the boil, then reduce the heat, partly cover and simmer for 25-30 minutes, or until the chicken is tender. Discard the star anise and cinnamon sticks.

Transfer the chicken to a board with a slotted spoon and shred into bite-sized pieces.

Return the chicken to the pan and add the noodles, sweetcorn, mushrooms, spring onions, carrot, mangetout and soy sauce. Simmer for 5 minutes or until the noodles are tender.

Garnish with the mint and red chilli and serve with extra soy sauce, if you like.

To make this soup Free on a Green day (and perfect for vegetarians), replace the chicken with 900g firm tofu cut into cubes. Add at the same stage as the chicken but reduce the simmer time to 5 minutes, then add the remaining ingredients as above.

leek, sweetcorn and roasted red pepper squares

serves 10

each serving is:

2 Syns on Extra Easy

2 Syns on Green

4½ Syns on Original

preparation time: 20 minutes

cooking time: under 1 hour

low calorie cooking spray

8 leeks, finely sliced

4 garlic cloves, peeled and crushed

2 red chillies, deseeded and finely chopped

800g bottled roasted red peppers in brine/vinegar, drained and finely chopped

600g drained canned sweetcorn kernels

15 eggs, beaten

100g Parmesan cheese, grated

salt and freshly ground black pepper

a large handful of finely chopped flat-leaf parsley

Banish the cutlery and serve these leek, sweetcorn and red pepper squares as stylish bites. This easy oven-bake recipe is a stress-free way to feed a hungry crowd – they'll be queuing up for the recipe!

Preheat the oven to 180°C/Fan 160°C/Gas 4.

Spray a large frying pan with low calorie cooking spray. Add the leeks, cover and cook over a low heat for around 15 minutes, stirring often, until the leeks are tender.

Add the garlic, red chillies, peppers and sweetcorn and stir-fry over a high heat for 3-4 minutes.

Divide this mixture between three shallow baking trays, each about 30 x 20 x 5cm and lined with baking parchment. Spread out to cover the base evenly.

Beat the eggs in a large bowl with the Parmesan cheese. Season well and stir in the chopped parsley. Pour this mixture over the vegetables in the prepared baking trays.

Place in the oven and bake for around 40 minutes or until the eggs have set and the top is golden brown.

Leave to stand for 15-20 minutes before cutting into bite-sized squares and serve warm or at room temperature.

roasted pumpkin, spinach and feta salad

serves 10

each serving is:

5½ **Syns** on Extra Easy

5½ **Syns** on Green

5½ **Syns** on Original

preparation time: 20 minutes

cooking time: 25 minutes

1.5kg pumpkin flesh,
cut into bite-sized pieces

low calorie cooking spray

1 tsp paprika

1 tsp cumin seeds

salt and freshly ground
black pepper

300g baby spinach leaves

2 red onions, peeled,
halved and thinly sliced

400g feta cheese,
cut into 1.5cm cubes

for the dressing

10 tbsp fat free French dressing

2 tsp mustard powder
mixed with 4 tbsp water

¼ tsp sweetener

juice of 1 orange

The combination of colours, flavours and textures in this roasted vegetable and tangy feta salad is a guaranteed crowd-pleaser. The tasty Free dressing works well on all sorts of salads, plus it keeps for a couple of days and is a doddle to make!

Preheat the oven to 220°C/Fan 200°C/Gas 7. Line a large baking tray with baking parchment.

Place the pumpkin in a large bowl and spray with low calorie cooking spray. Sprinkle over the paprika and cumin seeds and season to taste. Gently toss until well coated.

Place the pumpkin in a single layer on the prepared tray and bake for 25 minutes, turning once, until golden brown. Remove from the oven and set aside for 30 minutes to cool.

Combine all the dressing ingredients in a screw-top jar and shake until well combined. Season well.

Place the pumpkin, spinach, onions and feta in a large bowl. Drizzle over the dressing and gently toss until just combined. Serve immediately.

If pumpkin isn't available, this salad would also be delicious using butternut squash.

aromatic lamb and vegetable curry

Invite your friends round and cook up this show-stopping spiced lamb and vegetable curry. You can swap the vegetables to suit your personal taste, the season or whatever's in your fridge.

serves 10

each serving is:

Free on Extra Easy

½ **Syn** on Original

11½ **Syns** on Green

preparation time: 25 minutes

cooking time:
under 1 hour 15 minutes

Spray a large flameproof casserole dish with low calorie cooking spray and place over a high heat. Add the lamb and cook for around 5 minutes, in batches, until browned all over. Transfer the lamb to a bowl or plate with a slotted spoon.

Add the onions, garlic and ginger to the casserole dish and cook, stirring frequently, for around 10 minutes or until the onion is tender. Add the curry powder, cauliflower and carrots and stir to mix well.

Add the tomatoes, tomato purée and stock and bring to the boil. Return the lamb to the casserole and reduce the heat to a simmer. Cover and cook for around 1 hour until the lamb and vegetables are tender.

Add the peas and chopped coriander and cook for 5 minutes over a high heat or until the peas are piping hot. Remove from the heat, stir in the yogurt, season to taste and serve immediately.

Accompany with a bowl of yogurt sprinkled with chopped coriander.

low calorie cooking spray

1.5kg lean boneless lamb leg steaks, all visible fat removed, cut into 2cm chunks

2 medium onions, peeled and finely chopped

4 garlic cloves, peeled and finely chopped

2.5cm piece root ginger, peeled and grated

2 tbsp curry powder

600g cauliflower florets

4 large carrots, peeled and thickly sliced

3 x 400g cans chopped tomatoes

4 tbsp tomato purée

300ml lamb or vegetable stock

200g frozen peas

a large handful of finely chopped fresh coriander, plus extra to serve

250g fat free natural yogurt, plus extra to serve

salt and freshly ground black pepper

herbed pork escalope picatta

serves 10

each serving is:

1 Syn on Extra Easy

1 Syn on Original

11½ Syns on Green

preparation time: 25 minutes

cooking time: under 30 minutes

---

10 x 150g pork escalopes, all visible fat removed

salt and freshly ground black pepper

10 sage leaves

10 very thin slices of Parma ham

low calorie cooking spray

500ml chicken stock

6 garlic cloves, peeled and very finely chopped

2 shallots, peeled and finely diced

1 red pepper, deseeded and very finely diced

1 level tbsp gravy granules

a large handful of roughly chopped fresh parsley

finely grated zest of 2 lemons

6 tbsp small capers, rinsed

lemon wedges, to serve

Robust Italian flavours pack a punch and taste delicious in this Parma ham-wrapped pork picatta. This impressive main course is a great way to feed friends with the minimum of effort.

Place the pork escalopes between sheets of cling film and, using a mallet or rolling pin, beat lightly until about 1cm thick. Remove the cling film, season the pork very well with black pepper and lay out on a clean work surface.

Place a sage leaf on one side of each escalope and wrap each escalope with a slice of Parma ham.

Spray a large frying pan with low calorie cooking spray and place over a high heat. Add the escalopes and cook for 3-4 minutes on each side, in batches, until just cooked through. Remove from the pan using a slotted spoon and keep warm.

Meanwhile place the stock, garlic, shallots, red pepper and gravy granules in a saucepan and bring to the boil. Cook for around 5 minutes, until slightly thickened, then remove from the heat and stir in the parsley, lemon zest and capers.

Place the escalopes on a wide serving platter and spoon over the stock mixture. Serve with lemon wedges.

saffron rice with prawns and vegetables

This prawn and vegetable rice recipe is chock-a-block with flavour and is perfect for feeding a table of hungry mouths. It's Free on Extra Easy, full of Superfree veggies and, best of all, ready in less than 40 minutes.

serves 10

each serving is:

Free on Extra Easy

3 Syns on Green

10½ Syns on Original

preparation time: 25 minutes

cooking time: under 35 minutes

Spray a large frying pan with low calorie cooking spray, place over a medium heat and gently fry the onions and garlic until softened. Stir in the rice for a minute or so until it is coated.

Add the saffron, paprika, turmeric, cinnamon, green beans and peppers and enough stock to cover the rice (about two-thirds of the measured quantity). Stir well and bring to the boil, then turn down the heat and simmer.

Cook gently for about 10 minutes, stirring occasionally to prevent the rice sticking to the bottom of the pan. Add some more of the stock if it is being absorbed too quickly. Stir in the prawns and peppers and season to taste.

Pour over the remaining stock. Cover tightly with foil and leave to cook gently for about 10 minutes, until the prawns have cooked through and the rice and vegetables are tender. Sprinkle over the parsley and serve immediately with lemon wedges to squeeze over.

low calorie cooking spray

2 large onions, peeled and finely chopped

4 garlic cloves, peeled and chopped

600g long-grain rice

a large pinch of saffron threads

2 tsp smoked paprika

1 tsp ground turmeric

¼ tsp ground cinnamon

400g green beans, trimmed and cut into 4cm lengths

1 orange and 1 yellow pepper, deseeded and cut into chunks

2 litres boiling hot chicken, fish or vegetable stock

800g raw peeled tiger prawns, tails can be left on if preferred (thawed if frozen)

1 x 375g jar mild peppadew peppers in brine/vinegar, drained and roughly chopped

salt and freshly ground black pepper

a small handful of finely chopped fresh curly parsley

lemon wedges, to serve

mediterranean-style
stuffed courgettes

serves 10

each serving is:

1½ Syns on Extra Easy

5 Syns on Green

6½ Syns on Original

preparation time: 30 minutes

cooking time: 20 minutes

10 large courgettes
(about 230g each)

300g long-grain rice

4 ripe plum tomatoes,
deseeded and chopped

2 eggs, lightly beaten

4 tbsp chopped fresh mint

2 tsp dried basil

salt and freshly ground
black pepper

low calorie cooking spray

600g extra-lean minced beef

2 onions, peeled
and finely chopped

4 garlic cloves, peeled and crushed

500g passata

2 tbsp tomato purée

2 tsp finely chopped
fresh rosemary

60g Parmesan cheese, grated

Mediterranean-style courgette 'boats' filled with a hearty rice and minced beef stuffing make a satisfying main course – perfect if you've got a hungry horde coming over for brunch, lunch or dinner.

Preheat the oven to 190°C/Fan 170°C/Gas 5. Cut each courgette in half lengthways and scoop out and discard the pulpy centre with a teaspoon, leaving a shell about 1cm thick.

Place the courgettes in two shallow baking dishes or roasting tins, cover with foil and bake for 20 minutes or until tender – they should pierce easily with a fork.

Meanwhile, cook the rice according to the packet instructions. Drain, allow to stand for 5 minutes, then add the tomatoes, egg, chopped mint and dried basil. Stir to mix well, season to taste and set aside.

While the courgettes and rice are cooking, spray a large frying pan with low calorie cooking spray and stir-fry the beef over a medium heat for 5 minutes or until browned.

Add the onion and garlic and cook for a further 5 minutes until the onion has softened. Stir in the passata, tomato purée and rosemary, bring to the boil, then reduce the heat and simmer gently for 10-15 minutes.

Stir in the rice mixture and mix together.

Spoon the stuffing mixture into the courgette 'boats' and sprinkle with the cheese. Bake for 15-20 minutes until golden and crispy on top. Serve immediately.

spicy
penne salad

A tasty twist on surf 'n' turf, this hearty salad will go down a treat when feeding a crowd. The green chilli pesto packs a fiery kick that'll heat up your dinner party – and your weight loss!

serves 10

each serving is:

1 Syn on Extra Easy

6½ Syns on Green

10 Syns on Original

preparation time: 20 minutes

cooking time: under 15 minutes

500g penne pasta

400g green beans, trimmed and halved

300g lean bacon rashers, all visible fat removed

400g cherry tomatoes, halved

2 red onions, peeled, halved and thinly sliced

5 x 185g cans tuna steak in spring water, drained and flaked

for the pesto

2 green chillies, deseeded and finely chopped

100g fresh basil, roughly chopped

4 garlic cloves, peeled and crushed

50g Parmesan cheese, grated

200g low fat natural cottage cheese

200ml vegetable stock

salt and freshly ground black pepper

Cook the pasta according to the packet instructions, adding the green beans for the last 5 minutes of cooking time. Drain and rinse under cold running water. Drain again and set aside.

Meanwhile grill the bacon under a medium hot grill for around 5 minutes or until crisp. Cut into bite-sized pieces and set aside.

Make the pesto by placing all the ingredients in a blender or food processor and blend until well mixed and fairly smooth. Scrape down the sides of the bowl with a spatula and blend again briefly. Transfer to a bowl and season well.

Place the cooked penne and green beans in a wide salad bowl and spoon over the pesto.

Add all the remaining ingredients and toss to mix well. Check the seasoning and serve immediately.

Replace the tuna with
cooked, shredded chicken
for a 'meatier' salad.

herb-roasted tomatoes

For a Free side dish that'll knock the socks off your guests, serve these basil and thyme-roasted tomatoes. The sweet, tangy taste of the tomatoes will transform any dish into a Mediterranean masterpiece within seconds – mamma mia!

serves 10

each serving is:

Free on Extra Easy

Free on Green

Free on Original

preparation time: 15 minutes

cooking time: under 50 minutes

Preheat the oven to 160°C/Fan 140°C/Gas 3. Line two large baking sheets with baking parchment.

Arrange the tomatoes on the prepared sheets, cut sides up, in a single layer. Spray with low calorie cooking spray, drizzle over the balsamic vinegar and sprinkle with the garlic, sweetener, salt, pepper, basil and thyme.

Roast in the oven for 35-45 minutes until the tomatoes start to caramelise and the flavours concentrate.

Serve warm or at room temperature, garnished with the extra basil leaves.

1.5kg plum or vine tomatoes, halved lengthways

low calorie cooking spray

6 tbsp balsamic vinegar

10 large garlic cloves, peeled and finely diced

2 tsp sweetener

2 tbsp sea salt

1 tbsp freshly ground black pepper

large handful of finely chopped fresh basil, plus extra leaves to garnish

3 tbsp fresh thyme leaves

These tomatoes are freezer-friendly. Just place them in an airtight, freezer-proof container and freeze. Defrost whenever your spaghetti or pasta sauce needs a little boost of summer.

basmati and wild rice salad

This luxurious and filling rice salad makes a nice addition to a laid-back lunch with friends. Best made the day before so the herb dressing can infuse with the Superfree vegetables, it's delicious in lunchboxes, too.

Cook the rice according to the packet instructions. Allow to cool, then transfer to a large mixing bowl and refrigerate until cold.

To make the dressing, whisk the vinegar, mustard, sweetener, garlic, dried tarragon and chilli flakes together in a small mixing bowl until smooth. Season well. Pour the fat free French dressing into the vinegar mixture in a thin, steady stream while whisking vigorously until it has been fully incorporated. Set aside.

Stir the celery, chopped parsley, spring onions and tomatoes into the cooled rice. Stir in the dressing until evenly blended. Cover and refrigerate for a minimum of 2 hours.

Bring a small saucepan of lightly salted water to the boil. Add the sugar snap peas and cook, uncovered, until just tender – about 50 seconds. Drain, then immediately immerse in iced water for several minutes. Once cold, drain the peas and slice lengthways. Refrigerate until ready to serve.

Stir the peas into the rice mixture just before serving.

serves 10

each serving is:

Free on Extra Easy

Free on Green

9 Syns on Original

preparation time: 25 minutes plus chilling

cooking time: under 30 minutes

for the salad

500g pack basmati and wild rice

8 celery sticks, sliced

a small handful of roughly chopped fresh parsley

6 spring onions, thinly sliced

400g cherry tomatoes, halved

400g sugar snap peas, trimmed

for the dressing

5 tbsp vinegar

1 level tbsp English mustard

2 tsp sweetener

1 garlic clove, finely chopped

1 tsp dried tarragon, crumbled

½ tsp dried red chilli flakes

salt and freshly ground black pepper

10 tbsp fat free French dressing

apricot and peach meringue tray bake

serves 10

each serving is:

2½ **Syns** on Extra Easy

2½ **Syns** on Green

2½ **Syns** on Original

preparation time: 25 minutes

cooking time: 1½ hours

No summer soirée is complete without a show-stopping pudding and this apricot and peach meringue has certainly got the 'wow' factor. For 2½ Syns per slice, it'll spread a little sunshine to your guests and leave them feeling peachy!

for the meringue

5 large egg whites

1 level tsp cornflour

120g caster sugar

3 tbsp sweetener

for the topping

200g fat free natural yogurt

200g quark

1 tsp sweetener

6 ripe peaches, halved, stoned and sliced

8-10 apricots, halved, stoned and sliced

Preheat the oven to 110°C/Fan 90°C/Gas ¼. Line a large baking sheet with baking parchment.

Place the egg whites and cornflour into a large clean mixing bowl. Beat them with an electric hand whisk on a medium speed until the mixture stands up in stiff peaks when the blades are lifted.

Turn the whisk speed to high and start to add the caster sugar, a teaspoon at a time. Continue beating for 3-4 seconds between each addition of sugar until the mixture is thick and glossy. (It's important to add the sugar slowly as it helps prevent the meringue from 'weeping'.)

Sift a spoonful of the sweetener over the mixture then fold it in with a metal spoon. Repeat with the remaining sweetener. The mixture should now look smooth and billowy.

Using a palette knife, spread this mixture over the prepared baking sheet to cover evenly.

Place in the oven and bake for 1½ hours until the meringue sounds crisp when tapped underneath and is a pale coffee colour. Leave to cool on the tray or a wire rack.

Whisk the yogurt and quark together, add the sweetener and spoon over the meringue.

Mix the fruit slices together and scatter over the top of the yogurt. Lightly dust with icing sugar (1 Syn per level teaspoon), if you like, before serving.

Extra Easy Entertaining | *Feeding a crowd*

tropical fruit tart

serves 10

each serving is:

4 Syns on Extra Easy

4 Syns on Green

4 Syns on Original

preparation time: 20 minutes

cooking time: under 15 minutes

200g ready-made puff pastry

200g Total 0% Natural Greek Yogurt

200g quark

a few drops of vanilla essence

2 tbsp sweetener

2 kiwi fruits, peeled, cut into 1.5cm cubes

200g mango flesh, cut into 1.5cm cubes

200g pineapple flesh, cut into 1.5cm cubes

pulp and seeds of 3 passion fruits

Capture the charms of the Caribbean with this exotic fruit tart that's bursting with the sunshine flavours of kiwi fruit, mango, pineapple and passion fruit. At only 4 Syns per slice, it's a totally tropical way to bring your meal to a close.

Preheat the oven to 220°C/Fan 200°C/Gas 7. Line a large baking sheet with baking parchment.

Roll out the pastry into a rectangle about 34 x 10cm and place on the baking sheet. Using a sharp knife, score a border about 5mm in from the edge of the pastry.

Place the pastry in the oven and bake for 12-15 minutes until risen slightly and golden. Remove from the oven and leave to cool on a wire rack.

Meanwhile, mix the yogurt and quark together and add the vanilla essence and sweetener.

Push down the centre of the pastry to make space for the filling and spoon in the yogurt mixture.

Mix the fruit together and spoon over the yogurt. Serve dusted with icing sugar (1 Syn per level teaspoon), if you like.

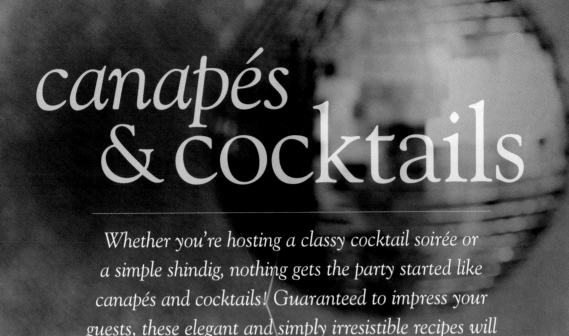

canapés & cocktails

Whether you're hosting a classy cocktail soirée or
a simple shindig, nothing gets the party started like
canapés and cocktails! Guaranteed to impress your
guests, these elegant and simply irresistible recipes will
quickly win a place in your regular repertoire.

beef and
lettuce cups

makes 16

each cup is:

½ **Syn** on Extra Easy

½ **Syn** on Original

2½ **Syns** on Green

preparation time: 10 minutes
plus marinating

cooking time: under 5 minutes

500g lean frying steaks,
all visible fat removed

4 level tbsp teriyaki marinade

1 tsp very finely chopped red chilli,
plus extra slivers to serve

1cm piece root ginger,
peeled and grated

1 garlic clove, peeled and grated

1 cucumber, halved,
deseeded and finely diced

2 tbsp each of finely chopped
fresh coriander and mint

juice of 1 large lime

salt and freshly ground
black pepper

low calorie cooking spray

16 little gem lettuce leaves,
separated

spring onion slivers, to serve

These will soon become a finger-food favourite,
with the lettuce acting as a handy little vessel for
the succulent beef and cucumber combination.

Put the steaks between two sheets of cling film and beat with a rolling
pin until they are half their original thickness. Slice the steak very thinly
and place in a mixing bowl.

Mix the teriyaki marinade, red chilli, ginger and garlic in a bowl then
pour over the beef and toss to coat the meat well. Leave to marinate for
30 minutes.

Meanwhile, mix the cucumber, chopped herbs and the lime juice in a
large bowl. Season well and set aside.

Spray a large frying pan with low calorie cooking spray and place
over a high heat. When hot, fry the steak slices for 2 minutes for
rare to medium or 3 minutes for well done, turning the slices halfway
through.

Arrange the lettuce leaves on two serving platters. Spoon the
cucumber mixture into the lettuce leaves, top with the seared beef
and sprinkle with the red chilli and spring onion slivers.

jerk chicken skewers

makes 24

each skewer is:

Free on Extra Easy

Free on Original

1½ Syns on Green

preparation time: 20 minutes
plus marinating

cooking time: under 10 minutes

Bring a taste of the Caribbean to your party with these spicy skewers. Marinating the chicken in the jerk seasoning overnight ensures the meat is fully loaded with flavour.

4 large skinless and boneless chicken breasts

1 tbsp sweet chilli sauce

3 tbsp light soy sauce

2 tsp jerk seasoning

½ tsp sesame oil

finely chopped fresh coriander and red chilli

lime wedges, to serve

Cut each chicken breasts into six pieces and place in a bowl.

Add the remaining ingredients (except the chopped coriander and red chilli) and toss to mix well. Cover and chill in the fridge for 3-4 hours or overnight if time permits.

When ready to cook, remove the chicken pieces from the marinade and place on a grill rack in a single layer. Cook under a preheated medium grill for 2-3 minutes on each side until cooked through.

Push a skewer in each piece, sprinkle with the chopped coriander and red chilli and serve with lime wedges.

crab and cucumber cocktail verrines

makes 8

each serving is:

½ **Syn** on Extra Easy

½ **Syn** on Original

3 **Syns** on Green

preparation time: 15 minutes plus chilling

cooking time: none

½ large cucumber, coarsely grated

juice of 1 lime

2 tbsp very finely chopped fresh coriander

4 sheets of leaf gelatine

400ml vegetable stock

200g fat free natural fromage frais

50g quark

6 level tbsp extra-light mayonnaise

2 red chillies, deseeded and very finely chopped

4 spring onions, very finely chopped

salt and freshly ground black pepper

300g fresh white crabmeat (or canned)

lime slices, to garnish

This clever little canapé is well worth the effort… the cucumber jelly, flavoured with lime and coriander, is the perfect base to the creamy crab topping. It's like a spoonful of summer!

Using kitchen paper, squeeze out any excess liquid from the cucumber. Put the cucumber in a bowl with the lime juice and coriander and set aside.

Meanwhile, place the gelatine in a bowl, cover with cold water and set aside to soften for 10 minutes.

Place the stock in a small saucepan and bring to the boil. Remove from the heat. Remove the gelatine from the water and squeeze out any excess liquid. Add the gelatine to the hot stock and stir to dissolve completely. Pour the stock over the cucumber mixture.

Tip the cucumber mixture on to a shallow baking tray and allow to cool. Chill in the fridge for 4-5 hours or until firmly set.

When ready to serve, chop the set cucumber jelly into little cubes and divide between eight cocktail glasses or tumblers.

Mix the fromage frais, quark, mayonnaise and most of the red chilli and spring onions together. Season well and spoon over the cucumber jelly. Top with the crab, scatter the remaining chilli and spring onions and garnish each serving with half a slice of lime.

seared tuna and pickled cucumber canapés

These mini mouthfuls of fresh, perfectly seared and flavoured fish are a delicious combination of tastes and textures: sweetened cucumber, crunchy seeds and meaty tuna – a carnival for your tongue!

Using a potato peeler, peel thin strips of cucumber (you'll need 16 strips) and place in a ceramic bowl.

Put the vinegar, chilli flakes and sweetener in a small saucepan and place over a high heat. When boiling, pour over the cucumber strips and leave to cool.

Spray a frying pan with low calorie cooking spray and place over a high heat. When the pan is really hot, add the tuna steaks and cook, in batches, for 1 minute on each side (you don't want to cook them through – they should still be pink in the middle). Cut the cooked steaks into 16 bite-sized cubes.

Place the black onion seeds on a plate in an even layer and roll the tuna cubes in them to coat evenly.

Thread each cucumber strip on to a small skewer or cocktail stick in an S shape, then skewer a tuna cube with each one.

Arrange the cubes upright on a platter to serve.

Always use the freshest tuna you can get for mouth-watering results.

makes 16

each canapé is:

Free on Extra Easy

Free on Original

2½ **Syns** on Green

preparation time: 15 minutes

cooking time: under 10 minutes

½ a large cucumber

6 tbsp white wine vinegar

½ tsp dried red chilli flakes

1 tsp sweetener

low calorie cooking spray

600g thick tuna steaks

4 tbsp black onion seeds (nigella seeds)

mini prawn and chilli bites

Juicy prawns combine with chilli heat and fragrant coriander to make these pint-size party nibbles a real taste explosion!

makes 16

each bite is:

1½ Syns on Extra Easy

1½ Syns on Original

2½ Syns on Green

preparation time: 15 minutes plus chilling

cooking time: under 15 minutes

600g raw tiger prawns, peeled and chopped

3 level tbsp extra-light mayonnaise

2 spring onions, very finely diced

2 red chillies, deseeded and finely diced

1 egg, lightly beaten

finely grated zest of ½ lime

2 tbsp very finely chopped fresh coriander

100g dried wholemeal breadcrumbs

low calorie cooking spray

Place the prawns, mayonnaise, spring onions, red chillies, egg, lime zest and chopped coriander into a large bowl and stir to mix well.

Divide into 16 portions and shape into balls. Cover and chill in the fridge for a minimum of 6 hours or overnight if time permits.

When ready to cook, preheat the oven to 180°C/Fan 160°C/Gas 4.

Place the breadcrumbs on a large plate and roll the prawn balls in them to coat evenly.

Place on a baking sheet lined with baking parchment, spray with low calorie cooking spray and cook for 12-15 minutes or until firmed up and lightly golden.

Serve warm or at room temperature.

grilled herbed mussels

Delicate tarragon, parsley and chives add extra depth to these seafood favourites – and the cheesy breadcrumb stuffing brings a subtle crunch. Use the biggest, freshest mussels you can find for flavour-packed results.

Preheat the grill to medium.

Spray a small frying pan with low calorie cooking spray, add the shallots and garlic and cook for 8-10 minutes over a low heat. Transfer to a mixing bowl, add the rest of the ingredients and season well.

Add a teaspoon of the breadcrumb stuffing to each mussel and arrange them on a large baking tray. Place under the grill for 2-3 minutes or until the stuffing is golden-brown and bubbling.

Line a serving platter generously with sea salt or rock salt and arrange the mussels in a single layer on the salt. Scatter the extra chopped chives and serve with lemon wedges.

makes 16

each canapé is:

½ **Syn** on Extra Easy

½ **Syn** on Original

2 **Syns** on Green

preparation time: 20 minutes

cooking time: under 15 minutes

low calorie cooking spray

4 shallots, peeled and finely chopped

2 garlic cloves, peeled and finely chopped

finely grated zest and juice of 1 lemon, plus extra wedges to serve

50g fresh wholemeal breadcrumbs

25g Parmesan cheese, grated

2 tbsp finely chopped fresh tarragon

2 tbsp finely chopped fresh flat-leaf parsley

2 tbsp finely chopped fresh chives, plus extra to serve

1 small egg, lightly beaten

salt and freshly ground black pepper

16 ready-cooked New Zealand Greenshell mussels (approx 500g in weight)

roasted tomato soup shots
with basil cream

makes 8

each serving is:

Free on Extra Easy

Free on Green

Free on Original

preparation time: 20 minutes
plus chilling

cooking time: 1½ hours

These mini glasses of chilled soup provide a
tangy, taste-packed punch, thanks to the basil
topping and subtle hint of hot pepper sauce:
a truly striking canapé to impress your guests.

for the soup

700g plum tomatoes

1 onion, peeled and
cut into wedges

2 garlic cloves,
peeled and halved

1 rosemary sprig, plus
extra sprigs to garnish

low calorie cooking spray

salt and freshly ground
black pepper

200ml vegetable stock

2 tsp chipotle pepper sauce

for the basil cream

4 tbsp dried basil,
plus extra to sprinkle

100ml fat free natural fromage frais

Preheat the oven to 160°C/Fan 140°C/Gas 3.

Toss the tomatoes, onion, garlic and rosemary in a roasting tin, spray
with low calorie cooking spray and season with salt and black pepper.
Roast for 1½ hours until tender.

Discard the rosemary sprigs and transfer the roasted vegetables to a
blender. Process until smooth, then strain the mixture through a fine
sieve into a bowl, discarding the skin and seeds.

Pour in the vegetable stock and hot pepper sauce, check the
seasoning and chill until ready to serve.

Make the basil cream by whisking the dried basil and fromage frais
together until slightly thickened.

Fill eight small shot glass with soup and top with a dollop of the basil
cream. Sprinkle the extra dried basil and garnish each glass with a
rosemary sprig to serve.

sesame soba noodle spoons

makes 24

each spoon is:

Free on Extra Easy

Free on Green

1 Syn on Original

preparation time: 15 minutes plus marinating

cooking time: under 10 minutes

1 tbsp pickled ginger

1 level tsp sweet chilli sauce

2 tbsp dark soy sauce

1 tsp sesame oil

2 tbsp rice vinegar

1 tbsp each of very finely diced red pepper, yellow pepper and spring onion

100g soba noodles

1 level tsp toasted sesame seeds

1 tbsp very finely chopped fresh chives

These Japanese-style noodles are brimming with flavour thanks to a marinade of colourful peppers, ginger and spring onion. Assembling the little noodle nests on to flat-bottomed Chinese soup spoons makes them a stunning centrepiece to a party.

Finely slice the pickled ginger and combine with the sweet chilli sauce, soy sauce, oil, vinegar and vegetables in a bowl.

Cook the soba noodles according to packet instructions. Drain the noodles, refresh in cold water and drain again.

Add to the flavoured vegetables in the bowl, toss to mix well then leave to marinate for 4 hours.

When ready to serve, take a small amount of noodles and create little nests using a fork (just like you would eat spaghetti), carefully placing each nest on a Chinese soup spoon.

Sprinkle with the sesame seeds and chives and arrange on a platter ready to serve.

If you can't find Chinese soup spoons, you can serve the noodles in small ramekins or bowls.

manchego cheese and veggie paella cakes

Enjoy a Spanish fiesta of flavours with these savoury bites, packed with traditional paella ingredients and mouth-watering Manchego cheese.

Spray a large frying pan with low calorie cooking spray and stir-fry the shallots for 3-4 minutes over a medium heat until softened.

Add the yellow pepper, carrot and courgette and cook for another 5 minutes until softened.

Add the rice and stir to coat in the mixture. Add the stock, saffron and sweet smoked paprika.

Bring to a simmer and cook for 20-25 minutes or until the rice is tender and almost all of the stock has been absorbed.

Stir in the petits pois, Manchego cheese and roasted red peppers and cook for another 2-3 minutes. Season well, stir in the chopped parsley then remove the pan from the heat and leave to cool.

Once the mixture is cool, divide into 16 portions, roll into balls and flatten slightly to shape into cakes. Place into paper cake cases and chill in the fridge until ready to serve.

These mini cakes can be prepared ahead of time and stored in the fridge until you're ready to serve them.

makes 16

each cake is:

1½ **Syns** on Extra Easy

1½ **Syns** on Green

4½ **Syns** on Original

preparation time: 25 minutes plus chilling

cooking time: under 40 minutes

low calorie cooking spray

4 shallots, peeled and finely chopped

1 yellow pepper, deseeded and finely diced

1 small carrot, peeled and finely diced

1 courgette, finely diced

250g paella rice

700ml vegetable stock

a large pinch of saffron threads

1 tsp sweet smoked paprika

100g frozen petits pois

100g Manchego cheese, grated

4 tbsp finely chopped bottled roasted red peppers in brine/vinegar

salt and freshly ground black pepper

a small handful of finely chopped fresh flat-leaf parsley

spring onion and potato rösti with salsa

makes 16

each rösti is:

Free on Extra Easy

Free on Green

2½ Syns on Original

preparation time: 30 minutes

cooking time: under 30 minutes

These small potato patties are a scrumptious addition to a party spread, with the piquant salsa really adding the finishing touch. Serve them straight from the oven for the tastiest results!

for the salsa

2 plum tomatoes, deseeded and very finely diced

1 red chilli, deseeded and finely chopped

1 small red onion, finely chopped

4 tbsp finely chopped fresh coriander

¼ cucumber, deseeded and finely diced

juice of 2 limes

3 tbsp fat free French dressing

salt and freshly ground black pepper

for the rösti

1kg potatoes (King Edward or Maris Piper)

6 spring onions, finely chopped

2 garlic cloves, peeled and finely chopped

2 large eggs, lightly beaten

low calorie cooking spray

Preheat the oven to 190°C/Fan 170°C/Gas 5.

First make the salsa by mixing all the ingredients in a bowl. Season well and set aside until ready to serve.

Peel and coarsely grate the potatoes. Dry the grated potatoes by heaping them on a clean tea towel, gathering the corners together, wrapping them up and squeezing to press out as much liquid as possible. Repeat this with a second clean tea towel.

Place the grated potato in a mixing bowl and lightly season with salt and black pepper. Add the spring onions, garlic and eggs and, using your fingers, mix to combine.

Spray a large frying pan with low calorie cooking spray and place over a high heat.

Divide the mixture into 16 portions, and spoon half of them into the pan. Pat down to give you eight rösti, each about 4cm in diameter. Cook for 3-4 minutes on each side and carefully transfer to a large baking sheet lined with baking parchment. Repeat with the remaining potato mixture to make 16 rösti.

Place both sheets in the oven and cook for 10-15 minutes or until golden brown.

Transfer the rösti to a serving platter and serve warm, with salsa on the side so guests can help themselves.

champagne
jelly shots

These pretty shots of Champagne sparkle are a party showpiece, especially when finished with stunning gold leaf.

makes 8

each serving is:

2½ **Syns** on Extra Easy

2½ **Syns** on Green

2½ **Syns** on Original

preparation time: 20 minutes plus chilling

cooking time: none

2 sheets of leaf gelatine

500ml Champagne or sparking white wine

2 tsp sweetener

edible gold leaf, to decorate (optional)

Place the gelatine in a bowl of cold water for 10-12 minutes until softened.

Heat 100ml of the Champagne or white wine in a small saucepan with the sweetener.

Remove the gelatine from the water and squeeze out any excess liquid. Add the gelatine to the Champagne and stir until the gelatine has dissolved. Allow to cool then pour in the rest of the Champagne and stir.

Pour into a shallow baking tray and chill for 3-4 hours or until set.

Remove from the fridge, cut the jelly into small pieces and spoon into eight chilled shot glasses.

Decorate with edible gold leaf to serve for that extra special touch.

mini jelly and custard trifles

makes 8

each serving is:

2½ Syns on Extra Easy

2½ Syns on Green

2½ Syns on Original

preparation time: 20 minutes
plus chilling

cooking time: none

2 x 11.5g sachets of sugar free
strawberry jelly crystals

100g strawberries,
hulled and sliced

400g low fat custard

400g fat free natural fromage frais

fresh mint sprigs, to decorate

edible gold glitter/sprinkles,
to decorate (optional)

Trifle's always a party favourite and this twist
on the traditional version serves up individual
mini puds with a glittery finishing touch.

Make the jelly according to the packet instructions and allow to cool.

Divide the strawberries between eight individual trifle glasses and pour
over the jelly to just cover. Place in the fridge and chill for a minimum
of 6 hours or overnight until set.

To serve, spoon the custard over the jellies and top with the fromage
frais. Garnish with the mint sprigs and sprinkle with edible glitter
(1 Syn per level teaspoon), if using.

*Replace the strawberries
with raspberries or
berries of your choice.*

classy cocktails

Add colour and pizzazz to a party with these fresh and fruity cocktails!

ginger, pomegranate and champagne cocktails

makes 8

each drink is:

4 Syns on Extra Easy

4 Syns on Green

4 Syns on Original

preparation time: 20 minutes plus cooling and chilling

cooking time: none

4 tbsp sweetener

7.5cm piece root ginger, peeled and grated

grated zest of 1 lemon

100g pomegranate seeds

a few drops of Angostura bitters

800ml Champagne or sparkling white wine, chilled

Place the sweetener and 300ml of water in a saucepan, bring to the boil and add the ginger and lemon zest. Cool, then strain and discard the ginger and lemon zest.

Allow to cool completely and chill for 3-4 hours or overnight if time permits.

Divide the pomegranate seeds between eight chilled cocktail glasses.

Pour the ginger syrup into the prepared glasses, add a couple of drops of Angostura bitters to each one and top up with the Champagne or sparkling wine. Serve immediately.

lime and watermelon margaritas

makes 8

each drink is:

5 Syns on Extra Easy

5 Syns on Green

5 Syns on Original

preparation time: 15 minutes

cooking time: none

800g watermelon flesh, seeded and roughly chopped, plus a few seeds and extra thin slices to decorate

juice of 1 lime

200ml tequila

50ml Cointreau or Triple Sec

2-3 tbsp sweetener

a handful of ice cubes

salt, to serve

Chill eight martini glasses. Place all the ingredients, including the ice, in a blender or food processor and blend for about 1-2 minutes.

To serve, scatter a little salt on to a plate and dip the rim of each chilled glass into the margarita mixture (to a depth of about 5mm). Dip each glass in the salt to form a salted rim then fill with the margarita mixture. Decorate with a thin slice of watermelon and a few watermelon seeds.

fruity cocktails

These fruit and fizz-filled cocktails make the perfect aperitif for party nibbles!

peach bellinis

makes 8

each serving is:

3 Syns on Extra Easy

3 Syns on Green

3 Syns on Original

preparation time:
10 minutes

cooking time: none

3 large ripe peaches, peeled, stoned and diced

1-2 tsp sweetener

400ml chilled Prosecco

300ml chilled sparkling water

Place the peaches and sweetener into a blender or food processor and blend until smooth. Press the mixture through a sieve and discard the peach solids in the sieve.

Spoon a tablespoon of the peach purée into eight Champagne glasses or flutes.

Mix the Prosecco and water and use to top up each glass.

strawberry shirley temple mocktails

makes 8

each serving is:

1 Syn on Extra Easy

1 Syn on Green

1 Syn on Original

preparation time:
15 minutes

cooking time: none

200g strawberries, sliced

ice cubes or crushed ice

8 tsp grenadine (pomegranate syrup)

750ml diet ginger ale

Divide the sliced strawberries between eight tall cocktail glasses.

Fill the glasses with ice cubes or crushed ice.

Place a teaspoon of the grenadine in each glass and top up with the ginger ale.

citrus and cassis cocktail fizz

makes 8

each serving is:

2 Syns on Extra Easy

2 Syns on Green

2 Syns on Original

preparation time:
5 minutes

cooking time: none

ice cubes or crushed ice

100ml crème de cassis

orange slices

600ml diet lemonade

Fill eight cocktail glasses with ice cubes or crushed ice.

Divide the cassis and orange slices between the glasses.

Top up with the lemonade and serve immediately.

index

Published in 2012 by
Slimming World
Clover Nook Road
Somercotes
Alfreton
Derbyshire
DE55 4RF
UK
www.slimmingworld.com

Created and designed by
Slimming World's publications team.
Editor: Allison Brentnall
Designers: Kathryn Briggs
and Fabiana Viracca-Butler
Writers: Rachel Kempton, Nicola Martin,
Rebecca Robinson and Jennifer White
Proof-readers: Beverley Farnsworth
and Oliver Maxey

Recipes and food styling: Sunil Vijayakar
Photographs: Gareth Morgans
Styling: Morag Farquhar

Front cover photograph:
Ginger, pomegranate & champagne cocktails
and lime & watermelon margaritas, page 222
Back cover photographs:
Roast tarragon & mustard chicken, page 95
Mixed seafood kedgeree, page 26
Bacon & beef sliders, page 146
Apricot & peach meringue tray bake, page 192

Produced in China by Sherwood Press.

did you know?

10p from the sale of this book goes
to SMILES. In 2012 Slimming World
donated over £100,000 to the NSPCC,
SMILES' nominated charity, from
book sales alone.